Haunted Lives

For Lotte

Haunted Lives

PETER MULLEN

ROBERT HALE · LONDON

© Peter Mullen 1996
First published in Great Britain 1996

ISBN 0 7090 5953 1

Robert Hale Limited
Clerkenwell House
Clerkenwell Green
London EC1R 0HT

2   4   6   8   10   9   7   5   3   1

Photoset in North Wales by
Derek Doyle & Associates, Mold, Clwyd.
Printed in Great Britain by
St Edmundsbury Press Ltd, Bury St Edmunds, Suffolk.
Bound by WBC Book Manufacturers Limited,
Bridgend, Mid-Glamorgan.

Contents

Introduction

Ghosts

'Do you believe in ghosts?' is a misleading question which begs the issue, rather like 'Have you stopped beating your wife?' There must be such things as ghosts, unless we are prepared to call *everyone* who ever claimed to see one a liar. But what are ghosts? That is the question. Are they visitors from the supernatural realm or the mere side effects of an upset stomach? Scrooge famously accused the ghost of Jacob Marley of being 'an undigested piece of cheese.'

There is a long tradition for belief in ghosts. Parts of the Old Testament record that ghosts are indeed the spirits or shadows of those who have died. King Saul, for example, visited a medium at Endor and asked her to call up the ghost of the prophet Samuel (*1 Samuel 28*). The ancient Israelites did not believe in heaven and hell in the classic Christian sense; instead they believed that when a person dies he goes into a place called *Sheol*, sometimes translated as 'hell' in the Bible, but meaning 'the place of departed spirits.' The ancient Jews thought that *Sheol* is located under the earth. So Saul's request to the medium at Endor was quite literally to bring Samuel up.

The ancient Jews thought that human beings are animated and sustained by the spirit of God, and this spirit is from the same Hebrew word as 'breath' or 'wind' – *Ruach* in the old language. It is based on a sort of common sense: when a person dies he runs out of breath. The spirit departs and the corpse is buried. They believed that the dead person, taken down into *Sheol*, gradually fades from reality and becomes literally a shadow of his former self. Another word for 'ghost' is of course 'shade'.

One view about the status of ghosts taken by Christians is that they are the souls of the dead who cannot find rest, who cannot find their way to God, and so they unhappily haunt – i.e. hang about – their earthly abode. These ghosts are not evil. They are not the same as demons or devils and they do not require exorcism. A simple prayer that they may find rest is usually sufficient to guarantee their safe journey homeward to God. I have often used such a prayer in the course of my ministry and there always followed an end to the haunting.

Sometimes a ghost may appear with a message. The theologian and biblical translator J.B. Phillips recounted a visit by the ghost of the deceased writer C.S. Lewis, which was intended as a comfort and an encouragement. Or again a ghost may be the spiritual remains of a person who was troubled in life or who suffered a violent death. Such a spectre may become attached to a particular place and be seen by visitors or the new householders. This is the origin of the belief in the haunted house.

In all these cases the ghost requires help from the living in order to attain peace. These ghosts do not come to frighten us: it is they who are unhappy and trapped. In the presence of a ghost, an appropriate prayer might take the form of an instruction: 'Go and find your peace with God.'

The Jewish teaching about ghosts and the Christian assessment of the status of departed spirits are frankly supernatural accounts. Some people reject such other-worldly explanations and prefer a scientific or quasi-scientific account of a ghost's nature and origins. Perhaps, according to these views, ghosts are an unusual sort of force-field or an objectification of psychological energy? Perhaps, that is, their appearance is governed by some law of physics or natural science which we only imperfectly understand?

It would be a bigoted and narrow-minded person who claimed there can be no such laws. A hundred and fifty years ago we did not know that there were such things as radio waves. Who knows what other strange forces there might be in the universe – forces of which as yet we have little or no understanding?

Although there seems to be a great difference in theory between religious and quasi-scientific explanations for ghosts, in practice the actual difference is not very wide. No doubt some reported sightings of ghosts are simply made up in order to impress us. Others may be put down to a trick of the light or to ordinary misperception. But take away all the cases of lies, hallucinations and optical illusions, there seems to be a proportion remaining of genuine sightings. It is not the appearances themselves which are in doubt and debated about, but the nature of the appearances. What *are* ghosts? remains an intelligent question.

Some psychologists, following the teaching of C.G. Jung, account for ghosts as aspects of synchronistic phenomena. That is to say their appearance is in some way timely. A ghost's arrival on the scene at a particular time and in a particular place may seem appropriate – just what you would expect in fact. If, for example, you are on the battlements of Elsinore and the ghost of your father appears, looking out of sorts and hard done by, then suspect murder most foul. The case of Hamlet is extreme but it makes the point that perhaps the most pertinent question is not, after all, 'What are ghosts?' but 'What is *this* particular ghost's purpose in appearing?'

To take the psychological explanation further, the appearance of a ghost may be a kind of visual, objectified personification of some turmoil or mental disturbance in the person who sees the apparition. Psychotherapeutic consultation may be the most appropriate course of action where this is suspected. The appearance of Samuel to Saul was a case in point: in the end it said little about the supernatural state of Samuel but a lot more about the mundane predicament of Saul. When Samuel's ghost appeared, it was to give Saul the bad news that he was about to lose the most important military conflict in his career!

Nearer home, I put the question about the nature of ghosts to my son Tom, aged fifteen. We were travelling in the car at the time over Ilkley Moor in a thunderstorm. 'Do you think all those who tell us they've seen a ghost are lying?'

'Some of them are, but not all. But I think ghosts are just, you know, in your head.'

'Which is more scary then: ghosts that really exist, or ghosts that are only in your head?'

'Ghosts that really exist, of course – if they do.'

'But a ghost that only "really exists" is just one more

object, just one other thing, out there in the world. A ghost that is in your head though is a part of yourself. I know which I find more frightening.'

He was very quiet for a long time after that.

The Devil or Satan

Spiritual authorities have always taught that there are two attitudes towards the Devil which the Devil himself likes us to have: he wants us either not to believe in him at all, or else to take a too-close, obsessional interest. Sometimes it seems we alternate between these two attitudes so that the Devil, if he exists, must be mightily pleased at the reception he is getting in the modern world.

If we refuse to believe in the Devil, then evil can sneak up on us and we make ourselves susceptible to a surprise attack. If we take too much interest in the things of the Devil, then it is possible to get caught up in evil and overwhelmed by it – usually with disastrous consequences.

In pantomime the Devil has pointed ears and he carries a huge fork. In popular mythology he inhabits a hell of fire and brimstone which is full of damned souls who are being tortured by repulsive demons – the Devil's henchmen. In the western tradition of spirituality, in the Hebrew and Christian Bible, the Devil is seen as a different sort of character altogether. The Jews of the Old Testament times believed that Satan is 'one of the Sons of God.' In the *Book of Job* for example, the Sons of God come to present themselves before the heavenly throne, and Satan comes too. Here Satan is not a wicked demon or one of Milton's fallen angels, but a sort of Counsel for the Prosecution – literally, a devil's advocate.

In old Jewish thought, Satan is the creature who serves God by testing, trying human beings to see whether, under pressure, they will remain faithful to God. So in the *Book of Job* Satan argues that Job loves God only because God has made Job rich – given him treasures, houses, farms and land. This whole book is the story of what happens to Job's obedience to God when Satan is allowed systematically to take away his earthly comforts.

The view of Satan as one of God's sons has its advantages: it makes the Devil subordinate to God as a character who was made by God. The Jews held an extreme view of God's sovereignty. 'There is none beside Him.' There was never any suggestion in the Jewish writings of the Old Testament that God and the Devil are two equal and opposing powers. Such a view may be found in Zoroastrianism, but it is completely alien to classical Jewish thought and the writers of the Old Testament would have regarded it as blasphemous to suggest that the Most High God has an equal.

Satan was thus regarded as the accuser, the tester of God's chosen people. This idea of God was translated into later Greek experience when the word for 'The Devil' is Διαβωλος *Diabolos*, 'The Calumniator' or the evil accuser. Hence the word 'diabolical'. In the later Jewish writings much more independence is given to the Devil and he appears not so much as one who opposes humankind on God's behalf as the Counsel for the Prosecution in a court where God alone is judge; instead he becomes a wicked spiritual power in his own right – or, as we might say, in his own *wrong*.

In the Jewish *Book of Wisdom*, the Devil is the wicked spirit 'by whom death entered the world.' *The Book of Enoch* interprets the *Genesis* story about 'the Sons of God who had intercourse with the daughters of men' *(Genesis 6: 1-4)* as an account of illicit sex which produced a race of giants, fallen angels, who were condemned by God to eternal punishment.

In the Christian writings of the New Testament, the Devil appears as the tempter of Christ. He is the one who wishes to pervert Christ's ministry by making him choose the path of self-aggrandizement. Christ resists the temptations in the wilderness and drives away the Devil by quoting scripture at him and by the power of argument based on an understanding of God's will. So in the New Testament the Devil becomes the enemy of God and his ultimate downfall is foretold by Christ. Jesus proclaims to his disciples that he saw Satan 'fallen as lightning from heaven' *(Luke 10: 18)*. And St John refers to the Devil as 'a murderer from the beginning' *(John 8: 44)* and as one who has considerable power – 'The Prince of this World' *(John 14: 30)*.

St Matthew's gospel prophesies that the Devil will be condemned at the Last Judgement and that he and all those who follow him will be cast into the eternal lake of fire. This is the origin of the picture of the Devil surrounded by the flames of hell. But the Devil is not in charge of hell, like some abominable chief stoker, he is himself a prisoner in hell in the punishment to which he has been condemned by God. The other New Testament writers, St Peter and St Paul, take a similar view.

In the first few centuries of Christianity, the Devil came to be regarded as a fallen angel and he is called Lucifer by St Jerome. It was the early Christian scholar Origen who first developed the thought that the sin by which the Devil fell from heaven was pride. Origen argued that perhaps one day the Devil might be reconciled with God – but this was not a view taken by the majority of the Church Fathers of the first four Christian centuries. Christian teaching concerning the Devil says that Satan's sin was his desire to be equal with God or to be co-equal – like a brother – with Christ.

In modern times, most theologians have argued against the idea of a personal devil – of the Devil as a being in himself – and they have suggested rather that he is a kind of metaphor or pictorial representation of the selfishness or sinfulness to which we are all prone from time to time. This is all part of the modern view which says that there are mythological aspects to Christianity which must be discarded if faith is to be possible in a scientific age. According to this view, Christianity is seen less as a supernatural religion featuring heaven and hell, angels and devils, and more as an ethical programme concerned with personal and social morality.

The psychologist Jung held a creative view of the Devil which, in a sense, goes back to the old notion of Satan as Counsel for the Prosecution. Jung saw the Devil as a manifestation of what he called 'The Shadow' – the dark side of each individual personality. For Jung the Shadow must not be cut off – sent to eternal damnation – but accepted if the individual is to achieve psychological health and equilibrium. This is a way of internalizing or psychologizing Origen's idea that the Devil may one day be reconciled with God.

According to Jung, the Shadow is the unacceptable part of myself which at first I try to deny – the excuse 'It wasn't me' – but which I must ultimately acknowledge and take responsibility for if I am to become a truly integrated personality.

Jung set great store by the fact that one of the early names for the Devil was Lucifer and that Lucifer means 'bringer of light'. For Jung this does not imply Devil worship. The light that Lucifer brings, psychologically speaking, is knowledge of my Shadow, of my dark side. And it is only when I accept that I do indeed have a dark side – that I can and sometimes do behave in an evil way – that I can begin to see myself as I really am. This is, for Jung and Christian teaching alike, the essential precondition for moral and spiritual progress.

The Christian theologian uses the words 'salvation' or 'redemption' to refer to this process. Jung, as a psychologist, preferred the non-religious terms 'individuation' and 'integration'. The process is the same: for some acknowledgement of the Devil or of our own faults is necessary to spiritual and moral development. Remember J.M. Barrie's famous play: Peter Pan was the boy without a Shadow, and therefore the boy who never grew up!

Satanism

Satanism began as an explicitly antichristian movement. Its adherents take an oath of allegiance to the Devil which is couched in terms extremely aggressive towards Christianity.

> My Lord and Master, Satan, I believe in you and worship you as my God and my Prince and I vow to serve and obey you all my life. I renounce the other God and Jesus Christ as well as the Church, its sacraments and its teachings. I promise to do what evil I can.

With its links to medieval superstition, demon worship and black magic, this form of Satanism sets out deliberately to parody, ridicule and debase the Christian faith. Satanists sometimes attend Christian Mass or Holy Communion in order to steal the wafer which is given at the altar and they use this in disgusting ceremonies when it may be mixed with excrement. Satanists occasionally break into churches and abuse the altar and the sanctuary by a performance of the Black Mass.

Satanists believe in ill-wishing or cursing people or things. Often rival Satanist groups curse one another, and they really believe in the efficacy of the curses employed. This practice sometimes leads to ironic consequences as when a satanic group, unable to free themselves from the curses of a rival group, call in a Christian priest to perform an exorcism. Needless to say, the priest is not told in advance that this request for his services comes from Devil-worshippers!

Remains of sacrificed animals and even of burnt and decapitated corpses have been found in English churchyards and cemeteries. Really, Satanism is a perverted form of true religion, an absolute parody and reversal whose prayer and constant incantation is, 'Evil be thou my good!' Practitioners are usually involved also in drugs and sadomasochistic sex. Recent reports in the press and on television have confirmed what has been known by the clergy for a long time: that Satanism is connected with some cases of child abuse.

Just how much supernatural evil is involved in Satanism is open to debate, and in any case one group of Satanists differs from another in its beliefs. But whether of supernatural origin or out of only-too-human lust and the will to power, Satanism is a disgusting and degrading practice, repugnant to Christians and non-Christians alike. It is not rife in the sense that there is a group within every parish, but obviously even one group is too many.

Often practitioners are affluent, career-minded people from the professional and management classes with houses in the leafy suburbs. But Satanism's appeal is to anyone bored and looking for kicks; so in our 'me' generation we might expect it to win converts here and there. There are those who are bored with mainstream religion, finding it to be too tame and not productive of sensational happenings. To these people scientific materialism as a creed may seem an arid alternative. So with money to spare for such diversions, some opt for the frisson and danger of a promised affair with the Devil.

The temptation should be resisted absolutely. The practice of Satanism always results in personal degradation and usually also in profound psychological disturbance within the individual, his family and friends. If, as I do, you accept the real existence of supernatural or metaphysical evil, you may also conclude that Satanism is the quickest way to invite demonic forces into your life. The sensible person – even one with no fondness for Christianity – will have nothing whatever to do with Satanism.

If Satanism provides a perverted thrill, it is by no means a cheap thrill. For all their invocations of the supernatural, Satanists have a lively interest in worldly things: in a word, money. They often make secret video recordings of their ceremonies and rituals, or they take photographs, so that participants may be blackmailed at some future date for their involvement.

In the 1990s, new developments in Satanism play down the anti-Christian element. Some modern Satanists argue that Christianity is now dead and so opposition to it is a waste of time and effort. These people therefore practise Satanism as a 'black' religion in its own right. In practice this does not turn out to be very convincing, for it would seem that even the Devil must require God and the whole Christian vocabulary in order to define his own title and role as the Adversary.

And that is a chief characteristic and criticism of Satanism, its negativity. St Thomas Aquinas taught that evil is banality and a *privatio boni*, an absence of good and a mere nothing. This does not mean that evil is harmless. On the contrary, nothingness is the most terrible prospect. I cannot repeat too often the advice to steer well clear of it and to report any suspicions you may have of its practice to a priest *immediately*. Besides, many of the activities and pursuits of Satanists are illegal, criminal acts – violence against the person, sexual perversions, bestiality and the desecration of churches and holy things. Any evidence you may come across of such activities should be given to the police.

Angels and Archangels

In the Bible and other traditional literature, angels are intermediaries between God and humankind. The Greek word αγγελος *angelos*, means 'a messenger'. So, for example, it is an angel who announces to Mary that she is to give birth to a divine child *(Matthew 1: 20)*.

Angels were also said to bring food and drink to Christ in the desert after his temptations by the Devil. And it was an angel who rolled away the stone from the tomb of Christ at the resurrection. Traditionally angels are believed to be spiritual, heavenly beings who are without sin and who enjoy constantly the vision and presence of God. In the first centuries of the Christian Church, the teaching about angels developed so that these semi-divine beings were classified into three hierarchies with three choirs in each hierarchy:

Seraphim	Dominions	Principalities
Cherubim	Virtues	Angels
Thrones	Powers	Archangels

Speculation about the precise nature of angels intensified in the Middle Ages when St Thomas Aquinas and other theologians argued that they are intelligences not fixed to a body. Each angel, according to St Thomas, is unique, a species in itself, and like no other angel in its essential character. Angels are thus immortal and incorruptible. Since they do not have bodies, they cannot really be said to be *in* a particular place, here or there; but they are said to influence people and events by applying their power.

The greatest difference between immortal angels and mortal persons is that while we can think of God only indirectly by prayer, scripture and the tradition of the Church, the angels know God directly.

'Archangel' means 'chief angel' and in the New Testament Michael is named as an archangel. Gabriel and Raphael are also mentioned as archangels in subsequent parts of Christian tradition. Although 'arch' means 'chief', the archangels are generally considered to belong to the third and lowest hierarchy in the realm of heavenly beings, along with the ordinary angels and the principalities.

Angels and archangels are said to join their voices with humans at the Sanctus, the sacred part of the Mass or Holy Communion.

Holy, Holy, Holy Lord God of hosts
Heaven and earth are full of thy glory;
Glory be to thee O Lord most high.

Tradition has assigned the archangels specific tasks.

Gabriel the Archangel – 'Gabriel' means 'man of God' – foretold the birth of John the Baptist and announced the conception of Christ to Mary, his mother.

Michael the Archangel – 'Michael' means 'like God' – turns up in a story in the New Testament in which he disputes

with the Devil about the body of Moses. Traditionally
Michael is seen as the protector of individual Christians
against the power of the Devil, and particularly as the
conductor of individual souls into the presence of God at the
hour of death. He is usually represented bearing a sword and
standing over a defeated dragon, the Devil. His feast day is 29
September – Michaelmas.

Raphael the Archangel – 'Raphael means 'God heals' – is
traditionally regarded as the heavenly power who healed and
cleansed the earth after it had been defiled by the fallen
angels, the disciples of Lucifer.

The idea of a guardian angel – as a particular spirit
watching over and caring for each individual – is to be found
in pre-Christian writings from as long ago as 2500 BC and
also in the works of the Greek philosopher Plato. Jesus Christ
said that children have protecting angels *(Matthew 18: 10)*
and a Christian text from the second century says, 'Every
man has his angel to guide him.'

St Ambrose believed that good Christians were deprived of
their guardian angels so that they might have a tougher
struggle against the powers of evil and so enjoy a greater
reward in heaven! St Basil thought that our sinfulness
distresses our guardian angels and drives them away – which
is bad news if you are counting on your guardian angel for
help in the struggle against temptation, against your Shadow.

Modern psychology has sometimes accounted for the
appearance of angels as a product of powerful human
emotions. So an angel might be alleged to have appeared over
a battlefield, as widely attested at Mons in the carnage of the
First World War. But which angel appeared at Mons? Was it
the Angel of Death? In pagan tradition there is a god or angel
of war in the person of Mars, and he also appears above the
scene of battle.

Whatever angels are in themselves – if they exist – they
usually appear in the cultural garb and trappings of
particular religious traditions. A Christian visionary will
therefore tend to see Baroque angels of the type depicted in
western art, while a Muslim will see an angel after the fashion
of his own faith and heritage. This is not necessarily a proof
that angels are 'only subjective'. You could as well argue that
God makes them appear in a form in which they will be

recognized. There would not be much point in a visitation which only provoked the response, 'Whatever's this?'

Cherubim belong to the highest of the three hierarchies of angels and, although in modern kitsch they are depicted as chubby babies, they were envisaged in Old Testament times as the ferocious attendants who guard the very presence of God himself. Representations of the Cherubim were set up over the Ark of the Covenant in the Temple of Solomon, 900 years before Christ.

Seraphim are the six-winged angels who appeared to Isaiah the prophet in the year that King Uzziah died *(Isaiah 6: 1-6)*. With the Cherubim, Seraphs rank highest in the angelic hierarchy. 'Seraphim' is a title derived from an old Hebrew word for 'to burn' and the Seraphim are those beings who burn for and with the love of God. These are reckoned to be, among all created beings, the closest of any to God himself.

Finally, it is important to make distinctions and to classify angels also by what they are *not*. According to Christian tradition, they are not the spirits of those who have died; and you do not die and 'become' an angel. Similarly, they should be distinguished from ghosts.

Perhaps the widespread belief in angels in a variety of religions and cultures arose out of the human perception of the great gulf which must exist between the limitless and perfect God and ourselves as very limited and imperfect human beings. The relationship of such opposites cries out, psychologically speaking, for some sort of intermediaries, a class of spiritual go-betweens.

Peter Mullen
York, 1996

1 'No One Should See *That* ...'

I was at theological college in the 1960s when the fashion in the training of priests was to separate the students as far as possible from ordinary life. It seems incredible now, but in those days it was the way things were done. There were consolations: for example, the colleges were usually set in some wonderful, out-of-the-way, spot, in glorious country-side, away·from the noise and rush of the industrial cities.

That most students would one day be ordained to work in precisely those cities reflects a methodological incongruity in those whose responsibility it was to train priests. I was at just such an idyll: Brasted Place in Kent, where Napoleon III had made his headquarters for a time towards the end of the nineteenth century.

Brasted was in the middle of rural vastness, the rich fields of Kent through which meandered narrow almost unused roads; orchards and planted woodland, meadows and melodious streams. It was sempiternal England. Here too were the Battle of Britain pubs where airmen from Biggin Hill – 'Biggin on the Bump' – and other airfields, had drunk, laughed, commiserated and exchanged banter. By a rule which seemed a particularly ripe piece of foolishness, we students were not allowed to visit the pub in the village – the White Hart – because, it was thought, this would somehow give a wrong impression. We were permitted to go to the pub in the next village, the Lamb, which none of us much liked and where the beer was not so good.

Strange to look back on these quaint regulations. A Brasted student might not visit the local pub on the eve of his ordination, but two days later he would have care and stewardship of parishioners who were deep into the problems of the real world. It was a policy which made naivete into a virtue. It has all changed nowadays of course.

Brasted was beautiful but unhealthy, idyllic but stultifying. There were thirty-three students and four staff – all male. In this environment, which seemed to run on pure testosterone, the Warden's wife and the housekeeper – plain women in their forties – seemed to beckon like the sirens of old Greece. The sex-starvation quotient rose as the ten-week term progressed and there was the usual horseplay, public-school style, and a smattering of furtive but not very enthusiastic homosexuality.

Monasteries are different. There, men have taken vows and they know why they are there. Celibacy is a part of life and vocation. But we were not celibate. We had taken no vows of abstinence or chastity. We were merely frustrated. Give it any explanation or gloss you like – the displaced psychic energy hypothesis is as good as any other – pent-up sexual feelings led to emotional and psychological disturbances of a profound kind.

Or was there something more palpably evil than that at work?

There were little epidemics of illness. Not contagious illness but different sorts of complaints – in one week a man had appendicitis, another pneumonia, two more suffered accidents in the grounds and a fifth fell out of a window. There was a feeling that things had gone wrong.

The college had two ghosts. One appeared several times on the landing between the sixteenth-century part of the house and the section added at the time of Napoleon III. This ghost was a clergyman or a monk. He would typically walk from the oldest part to the newer and at some stage on his outing he would vanish. Many of the men had seen him. He was nicknamed 'The Shuffler' because of the style of his walk.

I saw him once. I am certain of this. There was no doubting that you had seen him when you had – nothing ethereal or gossamer-like about The Shuffler. I saw him late one Sunday night in November 1964. The last chapel service of the day was Compline at 9.45 p.m. After that, men would get together in one another's rooms for coffee and theological discussion – or for the usual sorts of chat about politics, sport and women.

I was coming away from Philip Cairns's room at about half-past midnight when I saw a figure coming towards me along the corridor. He turned off to the right, and I walked past the junction where he had turned. I was sure it had been the Chaplain – perhaps himself coming away from a late-night discussion group or party. I was sure because the Chaplain always wore a cassock, and this figure whom I had seen turn off also wore a cassock. So confident was I that when I passed the junction I called out, 'Goodnight, Chaplain!'

When I looked the way he had gone, there was no one there. It could not, therefore, have been the Chaplain. It was a long corridor with no doors off to either side. If the figure in the cassock had been the Chaplain I would have seen him somewhere along the length of the corridor. There was no one.

The Shuffler never really scared anyone. He did not seem to be the frightening kind of ghost. He was just accepted about the place, as a cat might be – a mascot.

There was something altogether worse in the new chapel. This was the more frightening *because* it was centred on the chapel, for the common expectation is that religion casts out or disperses such phenomena. Not in this case. John Brogden, for example, saw this ghost and he was terrified and out of sorts for weeks afterwards. His close friends went so far as to say that, after this haunting, John was never the same again.

He was the devout type and he would often go into chapel by himself and spend an hour or more in prayer. He would do this before Compline so we all became quite accustomed to seeing him in his place however early any one of us might be in turning up for the service.

This particular night, the Sacristan, Michael Dyer, was on his way to the chapel as usual to light the candles, open the Bible at the proper lesson for the day and to generally make sure all was in order. He told a few of us later:

As I turned into the chapel passage, John came towards me, quickly; he almost walked into me. I'm sure he didn't even see me. His face was white and his eyes were wild – like someone in a horror film.

He was trembling and babbling quietly. 'Michael!

Michael!' he said quietly like that, twice. 'Help me. I've seen something that no one should see.'

I was terrified just by the *way* he said what he said. What was it? I daren't ask him. I got Stan Evans to light the candles and I took John to my room – it was nearest – He spoke quietly, almost under his breath. His face was the whitest you could imagine – like that paper.

I gave him a glass of port and asked him what the matter was. He said, 'I saw it, that's all. No one should see *that*. We're not supposed to see *that*.'

At all times he was quietly spoken. He wasn't calm. But he was quiet. He seemed to be panicking quietly. In shock, if you like. 'Don't talk about it, Michael,' he said.

The doctor was called the next morning because John had a temperature and he was babbling. He was given a sedative and he rested. In a day or two he was up and about again. He did not go into the chapel – not on his own, not even with the rest of us for the daily services.

Then he had consultations with the Warden and the rest of the staff. He announced that he was giving up his training, and within a week he had left. Of all the men I met in my theological training, I would say that John was the most religious, the most sincere. If ever there had been someone with no doubt beside his name about the rightness and strength of his calling, that would be John in my view.

A month later he was dead. He had put his head on the railway line.

What was it all about? Not the Shuffler. I still cannot rid myself of the sickening atmosphere conjured up by those words: 'No one should see *that*. We're not supposed to see *that*.'

2   Death Watch

'I've got a ghost in my church.' This was said to me by a colleague from a neighbouring parish in the days when I was Curate at Oldham Parish Church. Tim Gaunt was new to the area and, as a cleric who had spent some time in sophisticated West London parishes, he regarded the outlying village between Oldham and Huddersfield where he had come to be Vicar, as more or less medieval. The thought was probably encouraged in him by the fact that his parish boasted the finest Early English church in the diocese.

'Why did you come up here to the back of beyond, Tim?'

'Twelve years in the gin, frilly cottas and perfumed candles region, old boy, and you'd be due for a rest as well. But you're not listening: I've got a ghost I tell you.'

'Have you seen it?'

'Well, of course I have! How else could I be so sure of it?'

'Hmm. I take it you haven't seen God lately, but –'

'– But you're determined to spoil my story. It – he – is a real ghost, I tell you: the genuine article. And it's a priest.'

As a high churchman, Tim had put on a regular Wednesday evening service of Holy Communion: 'Maass', as he called it. And it was, he said, last Wednesday, after the dozen or so in the congregation had gone home, that he saw his ghost.

I was locking the chalice and patten away in the vestry, which, as you know, is by the side of the sanctuary. I thought I saw something move out of my eye corner, and, when I looked up, I saw him kneeling at the altar rail, deep in prayer. Profile – that's what I saw. He was wearing a cassock and cloak. A priest, of about fifty years old. 'Course, I didn't immediately think it was a ghost. I thought it must be a local parson – or a

visitor on holiday or something – who'd seen the door open
and popped in for a prayer.

So I turned off the vestry lights and walked out by the other
door into the nave. From there I *ought* to have been able to
see the figure at the rail. But there was no one there. Not
there, you understand but – and this is what gave me a 'fright'
– he was kneeling at the other side of the church entirely, in
the Lady chapel. Now, there was no way he could have made
that ground in the time available. And I would have heard
him. St Mark's creaks like an old barn.

I stood still for a minute. I had to catch my breath, I can tell
you. As I stood there – oh, for half a minute at the most – he
got up, turned towards me – I couldn't see his face for the
light behind him – and vanished. Not a sudden vanishing,
though. I don't know how to describe it: a sort of thinning out
of his figure until it was a mist ... and then nothing.

All this was said to me at the bun fight after a Deanery
Confirmation Service. Tim said he had asked the Churchwar-
dens and one or two other people whom he described as 'level
headed' in the parish of St Mark, if they had ever seen
anything. 'So you've seen him have you?' – the wife of one of
the Wardens had said darkly – 'Well, you'd better ask Canon
Langdridge, he knows all about that one.'

'*That one!*' said Tim. 'It was the way she said it –
definitely medieval!' Canon James Langdridge was Tim's
predecessor at St Mark's. He had retired and gone to live out
on the moors in a remote farm cottage which had been
bought and 'done up' by the Church Authorities. 'Well, then,
let's go and see him. I'll phone him, if you like. Maybe he'll
ask us for lunch – he does French cooking, you know.'

It was an excuse for a day out. Jimmy Langdridge's cottage
was positioned like the eagle's nest, high on the moors above
the sparse traffic of the Huddersfield-Oldham road which
curved away along the dried up river route. In the far distance
was the reservoir like a sheet of frosted glass. 'Fabulous, isn't
it?' said Tim. 'I'd no idea the north of England was like this. I
thought it was all *Coronation Street*, muck and brass. It's
romantic. Mahler country.'

The old Canon was at the door to meet us. 'Saw you
coming three miles away, boys! Come in and have something
to warm you. November can be like Siberia up here. I walked

to the top of the rise this morning and the hills to the east were as clear as can be. And that's a bad omen. You know what they say, "When you can see the Pennines, it's going to rain".'

'Yes,' I said, 'And when you can't see them, it's raining already.'

We went inside. There was a blazing fire and the room smelt of pipe tobacco and something unmistakeably French from the direction of the little kitchen. Jimmy Langdridge was huge and he had a resonant bass voice. In his younger days – up to reaching sixty, in fact – he had been wicketkeeper for his village team and earned the title 'bucket hands'. He was one of those rare souls who always gave the impression of invincible cheerfulness. Huge as he was, there was no doubting that, for him, the world was a magic garden. He had a laugh like a musical scale. It did you good just to look at him.

'So you've seen old Father Deathwatch, have you? That's what I call him. Come and tell me all about it while I finish off the lunch.' We took our gin and tonics into the kitchen where Jimmy wrapped himself in an apron the size of a cricket square. He began to bend over the oven and arrange various dishes, making little coaxing noises in a spectacular Yorkshire dialect of culinary French.

I can not adequately describe what we ate, except that it reminded me of a month I had spent in the south of France – not in the brassy coastal resorts but *à la campagne*, with its peasants' houses like elegant ruins: herbs and wine, mushrooms and mellowness and dappled light among the trees.

'You called him "Father Deathwatch", Jimmy?'

'And that's who he is, Tim.' This when he had swallowed his last mouthful and folded his napkin with the sort of finality that goes with rolling out the covers at close of play.

He appeared to me over a period of ten years or more. I saw him full in the face only once. He looked troubled. He was a priest all right – with a cloak for cold funerals. You'll need a cloak, Tim. Up here, I mean. It's not like Belgravia on Denshaw Tops.

In 1956 he appeared six times and that's when I discovered his purpose – if you can call it a purpose. It was the flu epidemic and a lot of the old folks died. I thought I noticed a pattern. The ghost appeared – saying his prayers at the altar rail – always eight days before a death in the parish.

And that became the pattern of the rest of my time there – another twenty-three years. You get used to it. But it was rather macabre. I'd see him and think, 'Who? Who's next?' Not being married, I'd no one to discuss it with. Certainly, I'd never mention it to the parishioners. And I wasn't one to run off to talk to bishops.

Of course, some of the old folks knew the secret. They knew that I knew as well. But there was never a word spoken. So, when did *you* see him, my boy?

'Last Wednesday, after Eucharist in the evening.'

The old Canon looked at his watch. 'And today's Tuesday. Day after tomorrow, then! Ah, well.'

'Did you ever try to exorcize the apparition?' asked Tim.

'Not formally. I used to pray for him – especially on All Souls Day. I'm sure he's not an evil presence. He doesn't *cause* the deaths of parishioners: he's just a signal somehow. But he always looked thoroughly unhappy – troubled, as I said before.'

After lunch we pulled on our coats and Jimmy took us to the very top of the rise – perhaps another one hundred feet above his cottage. 'You can see four counties from here,' he said, 'Yorkshire, Lancashire, Derbyshire and Cheshire.' His voice against the wind. His black overcoat neck to ankle.

He wore the same coat as he waved us on our way. A pipe in his mouth now. From the road back down to the reservoir, he was the perfect picture of a scarecrow.

We were quiet for some time, then Tim said, 'It's unsettling. I have to stop myself running through my sick list. Old Nellie Walker – perhaps it'll be her. Then I think, "I hope it's not Rosie Garbutt, the three year old who's just gone into Oldham General for an operation on her stomach." '

'He tells a good story, does old Jimmy,' I said. 'I wouldn't take it too seriously. You know how these things can get out of proportion. Perhaps it happened once or twice – at the most – this eight-day thing. And, you know, he's sort of embroidered it.'

'He does a good lunch as well.'

By the time we split up back in Oldham, we were laughing about the whole thing.

On Thursday morning at about ten o'clock, I received a phone call from Tim: 'The Archdeacon's just told me: they've found Canon Langdridge dead in his armchair.'

3   Mother And Baby

'I was brought up on the Yorkshire Moors,' said Sue Turnbull, 'and ghosts were just – well, a fact of life like the wind and the rain. They were a normal part of conversation. We all knew which side of the fell was haunted or which shepherd's rest – that's a little drystone wall shelter on the tops – was ghostly.

> The country expression for 'haunted' was 'visited'. My mother would refer to a place – she might be giving directions to a stranger – in that way: 'You'll be all right on the north side of the fell, but Coombe Tarn – they say that's visited.'
> As I say, we took it all for granted – ghosts and the like. There wasn't any supernatural. The supernatural was natural to us in the country. It wasn't until I grew up and came to work in Leeds that I realized ghosts were supposed to be from another dimension.
> Mind you, I never saw any. Not that I knew of. But I used to feel strange sometimes out on the hills at dusk. The gathering darkness used to cling to you somehow. And there was whispering. Now there you are you see: a townsbody would say it wasn't whispering, it was just the wind; but someone from the moors and fells wouldn't make any difference between 'em. That was wind? That was whispering? It was all the same.

Still, for all her ready acceptance of the spiritual side of reality, Sue had come to me deeply troubled. She had seen something, a horrible thing, and it had left its shadow. And what – it struck me at the time – is a ghost, but a shadow?

She and her family had moved from Starbotton, near Kettlewell in the Dales, to Silsden, near Keighley on the moors, when Sue was nine years old.

My dad was a farmworker and I was sort of labourer and message-runner right into my teens – when I wasn't at school in Silsden. I used to take orders for bits and pieces of produce out to all the farm cottages on the moor. I walked miles in all weathers. I'm going back to the 1950s.

When I got to be about fifteen, I was forever in my dad's bad books. We had these terrible rows. I wanted to go to the youth club and – you know – hang about afterwards like everyone else did. Dad was strict, though. Also, we were a mile and a half out of the village so it was half an hour's walk home from the club. Dad wanted me in at ten and I said that was unreasonable. Mother never said anything except, 'You heard what your dad said!'

Anyway, I asked her one day to help me with my dad – to persuade him, say it was all right for me to come in a bit later. She refused. I lost my temper and shouted – something awful like, 'You're no mother to me!'

She cried. She just broke down and cried. Dad came in and saw her in that state and just hit the roof. It was hell for weeks. Mother fell ill not long after: It was 1950, Asian flu time. She had to stay in bed. I felt terrible. It was as if her illness was all my fault somehow.

It was April and I was running more errands than ever. One day – it was teatime and I was dog tired – dad asked me to take some money to the Wrights' cottage, over the other side of the moor towards Howarth. I was late setting off and by the time I got there it was getting dark.

You come down a steep bit on the footpath from Silsden to the Wrights' place. And that was when I saw what I saw. Pauline Wright was halfway up the hill, away from the path and on the moor itself. She was digging with a garden spade. Then I saw her bury this … bundle.

I was horror-struck. I knew what it was. There was a white shawl. I just turned round and ran. I lied to my dad. Breathless, I was. I said there was no one in at the Wrights' – that I'd try again the next day. He just grunted and said he was going that way himself in the morning. I felt like saying – especially after what I'd seen – 'Then there was no need to send me, was there!' But I said nothing. I feared his tongue.

The next few weeks were a nightmare. Real nightmares at night. And Mother coughing all night, the light on. And the days – I dreaded to hear something … but I knew what I'd seen, you see. I should have spoken up. I know that now – perhaps it would have made things better. But I never opened my mouth.

Then one morning my dad said, 'Have you heard the news? There's the devil to pay – Pauline Wright's killed her baby and buried it on t'moor.' His words hit me in the face like a hot blast. Then mother got worse, a lot worse. The doctor was at the house every day.

I helped look after her and she seemed to be on the mend at last. It was never easy between us though, because of my outburst that day when I'd cursed her to her face, more or less.

Night and day. Daydreams and nightmares, they were all the same. Sitting up next to mother, with just her night-light burning, I just saw faces looming up in front of me. My mother's face one minute. Pauline Wright's the next. And when I did sleep I dreamt of babies crying.

Then in May, mother died. Double pneumonia. I cried for weeks. I knew I wasn't crying for her. I was crying for myself for what I had shouted at her that day. And it all got mixed up with what I'd seen – Pauline Wright out on the moor with her spade and that ... bundle.

It got so bad that I had to have the doctor. He said I was suffering from shock. He didn't know the half nor a quarter. And I couldn't go out of the house. I was scared, paralysed. I cooked and did for dad. But I couldn't leave the cottage to save my life. I was like that for months.

'I thought it was all behind me – and then this,' Sue said.

In the intervening years, Sue had been married and separated. 'Three weeks ago,' she said, 'the decree nisi came through and suddenly it hit me – clunk. I started to have the bad dreams about my mother again, and they were all mixed up with horrific visions of dead babies.

'It got worse and I was sure I heard a baby crying during the day as well. I went to see the doctor and he gave me some tranquilizers, but they just make me feel drowsy, only half alive; and then I'm less in control than ever.

'There's something in the house, Vicar. I know it. Something's followed me all these years, from that horrible day on the moors. I know it has.'

She broke down and sobbed.

When she had recovered a little, I said, 'You're convinced that these bad feelings –'

'It's more than feelings. It's a presence, Vicar. It's a presence – in the house, I tell you!'

'Well,' I said, 'this presence then. You're convinced it has something to do with Pauline Wright and her child aren't you?'

'That's what it is. That's just what it is – the baby all white-faced and black-eyed and its poor mother, roaming around restless, weeping. It's so horrible. I can't take any more. I want you to exorcize the house, me – anything ... anything to take it away for good.'

'I'll come and bless the house, certainly. And I'll bless you, now, this minute.'

I asked her to kneel and I said the words, 'In the name of the Father, and of the Son and of the Holy Ghost' and traced the sign of the Cross on her forehead. She was calmer.

I said, 'But I don't think it's an exorcism the house needs – you neither. I think you're looking in the wrong place for the source of this trouble. You loved your mother very much, didn't you?'

'I did. And I can never forget how awful I was to her that day about coming home late.'

'That was just before she fell ill, wasn't it? And she never recovered.

'That's what's so terrible. You blame yourself – not just for upsetting your mother by being rude to her, but you blame yourself because she died.'

'How can I? It wasn't my fault. And yet – you're right. There's something in me – I don't know – but it seems to say, "It was your fault, Sue: your fault your mother got ill and died." You see, she was never really well again from that day onwards. But no – what am I talking about? – the thing that really upsets me is that dead baby and the lonely, guilty woman.'

'Aren't you the guilty woman, Sue? In your own mind, I mean – because, as you say, you weren't the cause of your mother's death.'

She became very quiet and thoughtful. She went and stood by the window. She was as she looked: a slender, beautiful woman who had suffered until it showed in her expression and her gestures.

'Will you do something for me?' I said. 'Will you go home now? And when you say your prayers, leave a little time over at the end to say sorry to your mother for upsetting her. Will you come back to see me on Friday, in the afternoon?'

She gathered her things and thanked me in the embarrassed style of one who has wasted someone's time. But she said she would come again on Friday.

Friday came, but Sue didn't. On the Sunday, she came to the early service – the eight o'clock when there aren't many in the congregation. She asked if she could have a word afterwards. We stood by the lychgate in the mist.

It's all over Vicar. Thank you. The most wonderful thing has happened to me. I did as you said. I said my prayers on Thursday night downstairs in the front room, last thing. And I added that bit you said – saying sorry to my mother.

When I looked up, she was sitting there – with a ball of pink knitting in her arms. She smiled. She said – but not aloud, if you know what I mean – she said, 'I've forgiven you long since, Susan. And I'm very happy where I am now. Everybody is.'

I said, 'Mother' out loud like that, and startled myself with the sound of my own voice. And she vanished. Not suddenly. But she just faded. She was smiling the whole time.

I'm sorry I didn't come to see you on Friday, Vicar, but I slept the whole day – the best sleep I've had in years.

4 We Disturbed Someone's Grave

St Paul's Church is between Sevenoaks and Riverhead in Kent, just off the A25. I was a student at the theological college nearby, and St Paul's was the place where we all met for Evensong on Sundays. The wide aisle, the gothic arches and the medieval stained glass combined to make a welcome change from the modern chapel with its clean lines and sparse decoration which was our milieu for the rest of the week.

The Vicar of St Paul's, Peter Royston, was a keen amateur actor. In his day, he had been more than an amateur; and, when he was in the mood, he would regale the students with tales of how he had shared the stage in the West End with Sir Donald Wolfit and, on one occasion, with Michael Hordern. Peter had come to ordination in mid-life, but he had been unable to leave his stage-struck past entirely behind him.

He was forever trying to get his parishioners to act in a Passion Play or in something lighter for Christmas and, now and then, in a whodunnit. Naturally, he regarded theological students as likely stage-fodder: 'Come on, don't be shy. You know you'll enjoy it. And the stage is the best preparation for the preacher: we're all actors, you know.' His big red face more than half-covered in white whiskers.

One October evening he was even more enthusiastic than usual. 'Oh look at this – it's a sure-fire success if ever I saw one. And it'll pack 'em in the church hall!'

He had been reading old newspapers about the parish at the end of the last century when there had been a series of murders – nothing random or indiscriminate: the victims were all members of the same family. 'The daughter did it', was the verdict. And Emily Tanner, aged twenty-nine, was hanged at Maidstone Prison in 1893.

Emily – something of a beauty, by all accounts – always protested her innocence but the testimony against her was so great and the circumstantial evidence so strong, that no jury could have done other than bring in a conviction. The tale had passed into local lore.

Peter had read up about the original police investigation and the trial and out of these he had concocted a play in two acts, enticingly called: *The Riverhead Poisoner*. He wanted three or four of us to take parts in it and others to help stage-manage, find props, paint, prompt or publicize in aid of his epic. 'It'll be fun,' he kept saying. 'It'll be fun.' It was at least an opportunity for some of the unattached theological students to associate with the young ladies of the parish.

As soon as we began rehearsals, things went wrong. Peter had had all the scripts copied and one night they went missing. They turned up again, but in a place nowhere near where he claimed he had put them. Other things, little things – hard to account for: an exploding light-bulb is nothing out of the ordinary; but *six* bulbs in one week?

It was a well-crafted play. The Vice-Principal of our college played Emily's father who defended her to the last, and Peter himself took the part of the tenacious Detective Inspector Whitton who was chiefly responsible for assembling the case against her.

The minor accidents became a running joke. To be truthful, we were glad to let our nervousness find outlet in amusement. Then, in the week of the dress rehearsal, events took a more serious turn. Cathy Wood, who played Emily's mother, broke her arm in a riding accident and had to cry off. Three of the cast laboured under heavy colds and Peter came in one evening to croak, 'Well, this is the first time in thirty-odd years that I've come near to losing my voice.'

Less well-defined, but telling all the same, there was an ominous atmosphere. It was not scary in the sense of make-you-jump-scary, but more like bad feeling – as if everyone was having to struggle against getting depressed and dispirited. The church hall did not feel like a comfortable place to be in – especially if you happened to be there on your own as I was on several occasions.

I was looking after the lights and there were little tricks of wiring to be done with adaptors, fuses and leads. This work could not be done while rehearsals were in progress, and the days were packed with study and tutorials, so I had to come back late in the evenings when the rest of the cast had gone home.

Maybe church halls are weird anyhow? All that rural creepiness. The depth of the countryside. Thick silence and late evening mists – some of the mist seeping in under the door. And the cracking noises given off by beams as they cool down.

The night before the final rehearsal found me up on a tall ladder fixing the central spot. I saw something down and to the side: something yellow, scuttling about quite noiselessly. Just a movement in the corner of the eye, that was all. But it happened again ... and then again.

I pinched myself against my nervousness and gave myself a stern little lecture. Then I got on with the job. It must have been after ten o'clock when I saw the yellow ... the yellow what? The yellow *movement* is about the nearest I can get to it. It moved away to the back of the stage. I almost fell from the top of the ladder. No sooner had I collected myself than the ladder began to shake so violently that I thought I was in for a fall. Then abruptly it stopped. I almost wished that I had fallen. A simple fall was something I thought I could cope with. Instead, there I was, alone, at the top of my ladder, and wondering if it would begin to shake again at any moment. Just then I heard a deep sighing coming from the wings.

I fell into a blind terror. I could neither run nor stand still. I merely shook and the ladder shook with me. After what seemed like half a lifetime, the sighing stopped. I waited. There were only the two stage lights on and the rest of the hall was a misty blackness. I waited. When I had ceased shaking enough to trust my foothold, I started down the ladder. My teeth were actually chattering, banging together like crashed gears. And I had always thought that chattering teeth were only a figure of speech, a dramatic device. Not that night, they weren't!

I reached the floor and stumbled to the back of the hall, near the door. Here I could switch on the rest of the lights. I did so. My plan was then to return to the front, put out the stage lights, walk to the back again, switch off the main lights, shut the door behind me and run.

I got as far as the stage on the right-hand side, found the light switch and turned off the two stage lights. My heart was in my throat. Little lights – products of my own terror – danced in front of my face. I began to walk to the back again, to the door and freedom from the creepiness. The horrible sensation that someone was about to lay a hand on my shoulder as I walked in the dusty quiet.

But it wasn't quiet the whole time. There came the sighing again, and this time it was more like a wheezing sound. I did not hang about to make any further investigations.

I turned up for the dress rehearsal and there was an atmosphere not of expectancy and excitement but of sheer gloom. No one wanted to do the play any more – not even Peter. Of course, he soldiered on: a true thespian, the genuine article would do nothing else except soldier on. But his heart wasn't in it. The others felt the same.

It was then that I saw the stage costumes for the first time. 'That yellow cape,' I said – last night's fear upon me again like an electric shock.

'Yes,' said Peter. 'What of it? Emily wore it all through the trial. She had trouble with her lungs – it might even have been the early stages of TB. Wheezed so much that the jury could hardly hear her evidence at times – so it says in the old copies of *The Gazette*.'

I didn't say anything to anyone. They were well enough down in the dumps already. The whole thing went off like a damp squib. The expected audiences never materialized: there were twenty or thirty there each evening at the most. Worse, there was no élan, no joy in it at all – not even, as I said, for Peter, the great enthusiast and prime mover.

After we had closed, I took him on one side in the pub and told him my tale. His response was deadpan: 'I'm not surprised. It was a mistake. Once we'd started, it was as if we'd disturbed someone's grave.'

5   John Lennon, the Pope and the Windsor Fire

Over the years, I have met a few people with psychic gifts which have shown themselves as powers of intuition, healing, telepathy or foreknowledge. Usually such people possess their gift moderately; that is to say, they cannot always heal a sick or a sad person; or they are not able to see the future in all its detail. But I do know one woman who is blessed – or cursed, it depends on your point of view – with psychic awareness to an astonishing degree.

Barbara Garwell, a housewife in Hull, Yorkshire, has received clairvoyant visions all her life.

When the Second World War broke out, her father, being too old for the armed forces, became an emergency firewatcher and nightwatchman. He was stationed at the local undertakers, of all places. One night, Barbara was lying in bed when she 'saw' her father. She told me: 'I knew at once that he was in great peril. It was so vivid. Light and fire and noise. I screamed and woke up the whole house. My mother was terrified and wondered whatever was the matter.

'I told her my father was in danger. I knew he was. He was too. He was late home. The undertaker's had received a direct hit and Dad was lucky to escape alive.'

Hull, as a port, was a target for the bombers. Barbara's mother's sister – Aunt Nell – lived in Newark in Nottinghamshire and it seemed a good idea for Barbara, aged about fourteen by this time, to go and live with her so as to be out of danger for at least some of the time.

Aunt Nell was not in very good health and really she needed some help around the house. So I suppose I came in useful – especially since my uncle couldn't do much to help his wife:

he was a retired army officer and he had taken on a subpostmaster's job in Newark.

So I went to Newark to help Aunt Nell. I learned everything there was to learn about postal orders and stamps and I helped around the house. I suppose my aunt and uncle were quite well off. Certainly they were a lot better placed than any of us in Hull. I could have anything I wanted. They were so kind, having no children of their own. But I was homesick and I began to brood.

One day – it was a hot day in June – I told Aunt Nell I was going for a walk and that I wouldn't be longer than half an hour. I walked down to the lane and past the main road which ran beside the barracks. I always used this road as a landmark so I knew I couldn't get lost. But strangely – it was June, remember – a thick mist came down and, as I walked, I very soon had no idea of my whereabouts.

I was still brooding, feeling homesick and sad. I walked on and on in the mist, far further than I had ever intended. Suddenly, I felt something or someone pulling on my left arm, and I heard a voice call out of the fog: 'Stop! that's far enough.'

I stopped dead in my tracks. One pace more and I would have walked into the river. That was amazing enough, but equally amazing was that I found my way back to Aunt Nell's house though the fog at no time lifted.

'Where have you been?' asked Aunt Nell. 'You've been gone nearly three hours!'

Nearly three hours! Where had I been indeed? To me, it had seemed like twenty minutes or so – that's all.

Barbara was convinced that guardian angels had saved her from stepping into the river.

Her next premonition occurred in 1945 when she was fifteen. She awoke at two o'clock in the morning with the sensation that she was in Northern Ireland. In a kind of waking vision, she saw an aeroplane nosediving. There was a frightful din and an ear-shattering screaming of engines.

The next thing I saw were dead bodies partly covered under hessian cloth. A voice said out loud, 'Eighty bodies!' Strangely – it seemed like a black comedy, a charade in bad taste – I then saw three men in the cockpit and over their heads was a rugby ball. In the morning I told my dad what I had seen.

There was nothing in the newspapers about a plane crash. I remember it was Sunday. Then, on the one o'clock news, it was announced: a plane had crashed in Northern Ireland and eighty people had been killed.

I called out to my dad, 'But the survivors – what about the survivors?'

He said, 'There's nothing about any survivors.'

But I knew there must be. I knew there would be survivors. And so it turned out. Three of them. The plane passengers had been to a rugby match. And there – hadn't I seen a rugby ball above their heads?

Barbara wrote down some of her visions in advance of the happenings to which they referred, and the documentary evidence is in the care of a consultant psychologist who regularly produces the written prophecies to visitors and researchers who come to him asking for proof. Over the years a pattern to the predictions has developed: often Barbara 'sees' happenings three days or three weeks before they occur. For example – and this case is documented by the psychologist, Dr Hearne – Barbara prophesied President Sadat of Egypt's assassination precisely twenty-one days before it took place.

I would not say that all, or even most, clairvoyants are fakes: but the trade does have its share of charlatans. Some of these are very clever people – masters (more usually, mistresses!) of the art of making a little go a long way. Many a fortune-teller will say, 'I see a tall, dark stranger' and the client rejoices in a prediction fulfilled when the man who delivers her new gas cooker turns out to be a six-foot Geordie with a black beard and a beer belly. Another favourite among pieces of alleged 'foresight' is: 'You will make a journey over water.' But this is hardly to be reckoned as fulfilled when I find myself on the boating-lake in the local park with a couple of grandchildren.

By contrast, Barbara's premonitions are always startlingly precise. For instance, she told me.

On 9 December 1980, I dreamt I saw the ex-Beatle John Lennon walking down a great flight of stairs with a stethoscope around his neck. The scene changed and I was a patient lying in a hospital bed. Lennon came into the room. He was still wearing the stethoscope. I woke up out of the dream altogether and very suddenly.

There was John Lennon in my bedroom, at the bottom of

my bed. I knew at once that something dreadful had happened to him. Next morning, I heard on the news that he had been murdered outside his New York home by Mark David Chapman. In the days following, the full details of this terrible killing became known and I realized he had died at more or less the same time as he had appeared in my bedroom.

Why the stethoscope? Why not a gun or an axe? I cannot answer that except to say that a stethoscope might represent a struggle for life, a last desperate attempt to discover life in his body. Alas, it was not to be.

Barbara Garwell is a devout Roman Catholic. On 9 May 1982, she was getting into bed at about eleven o'clock in the evening when she began to 'see' the outline and battlements of a spectacular castle.

It was exotic and it had atmosphere. It wasn't just any old ruin. Out of the castle trooped eight choirboys, or they may have been altar boys. At any rate they were dressed in some sort of liturgical costume.

There were crowds – crowds as in a noisy dream. Thousands of people and confusion on a grand scale. People were running in all directions and calling out anxiously, but no one seemed to know what to do. In the middle of all these people, there was a figure in white – obviously a dignified person, a person of State. I was certain that it was the Pope.

Three days later, at the Shrine of Our Lady of Fatima in Portugal, a man emerged from the seething crowds and tried to stab Pope John Paul II with a bayonet.

A royal palace featured in one of Barbara's recent visions. On 17 November 1992, she dreamt about the Queen Mother who was standing distraught, her hands clasped in front of her, while behind her a great palace was ablaze. Three days later, there occurred the disastrous fire at Windsor Castle.

I asked Barbara how she felt about her possession of this gift of foresight which must be very disturbing at times. She said, 'It's a great comfort in a way, even when what I foresee turns out to be a catastrophe. For it seems to demonstrate that the feelings we have about the world are somehow wound up with the world itself – with its fabric, if you like. And that makes me believe that my hopes and fears, all our hopes and fears, are aspects of an eternal pattern of which my visions are only a small part.'

6   The Clock Man

I was invited to say prayers in the school assembly on the last
day of term in Oldham Infants and Juniors. The teachers
always called it D-Day – the 'D' was for Deliverance. It was
wet. Rain is the worst sort of weather when it comes to
educational considerations for, while children become
subdued and biddable in fog and mist, happy in sunshine and
cheerfully exuberant in the snow, rain makes them irritable
and peevish.

Miss Kelsey had just called out to 4Y the dreaded words,
'Wet Playtime!' This meant that, rather than run out into the
school yard and get so wet that steam rose from their
pullovers for the rest of the day, the children were allowed to
stay in the classroom and do 'sensible' things like drawing
and painting. They might even play a game of draughts or
snakes and ladders. That was the theory but there was, it has
to be admitted, some falling off from this ideal.

Something about rainy weather makes it impossible for
young children to sit still. And, if it gets so dark that the lights
have to be switched on, they go wild as if it were bedtime and
they were at their usual game of demonstrating how wide
awake they could be, and not in need of sleep at all.

The teachers at Oldham Juniors were in need of sleep. It
had been the week of school parties and two performances of
the Nativity play, Parents' evenings and class reports. Now at
last it was D-Day and they looked as if they were members of
a bedraggled platoon on an enemy beach, helpless to do
anything except wait for the hour of their liberation.

Janet Kelsey was on our Parochial Church Council and I
had just called into her classroom to let her know that that
evening's meeting had been postponed. She was delighted.

The classroom resembled an aviary or a monkey house: wild activity punctuated by strange sounds. But they were, on the whole, amiable monkeys in 4Y.

As we were talking a little boy with red hair came out and handed Janet a Christmas card which he had designed and written himself. 'Oh, that's the nicest thing, Benedict. How very kind of you!' And a few more phrases of teacherly talk. Benedict stood still for a minute with his hands behind his back, looking as if he might either laugh or cry; his face turning as red as his hair. Janet said, 'Thank you!' three or four times more, and at last the little lad took the hint and trotted off back to his place.

There was enough of a genial hubbub for Janet to tell me quietly the strangest things about young Benedict. 'D'you know him, Peter?' Well, I couldn't say I knew him. I think I'd said hello to him in the corridor once or twice and certainly, with that red hair, he was always eminently visible in assembly: like a robin among sparrows.

'He's been here before, that one,' she said, 'Or else he's magic. He's seven, you know – that's all. But when it's story time, or I ask the children to tell us their news, he has them all spellbound. Me too. He's leaving Oldham today. His father works for a television company and they're moving down south.'

She told me a tale Benedict had, as she put it, 'come out with' a few weeks earlier. 'I was wondering whether I should tell him to shut up – really! I mean, he was frightening them. He was frightening me, I can tell you. The hairs were standing out on the back of my neck.'

It wasn't just the story, but the way he told it. Spellbinding – it's the only word for it. Anyhow, he said he wanted to tell us about the Clock Man – that's the man he says lives inside the clock on the Parish Church. Now then, I bet you didn't know you had such a ghostly lodger did you, Peter?

Benedict said that at night the clock tower moved out of the churchyard and over Oldham Edge to his house on the St Stephen's estate. He said the clock halted outside his front door and then the Clock Man stepped out of the mechanism.

What was he like? That's the scary bit: he had a long black cloak which covered him from head to toe; but he had no face. He told Benedict things – things that were going to

happen. For instance he told him the night before about the
fire that gutted Kellet and Hargreaves shop in town. He also
said that Andrea Thompson was going to get German measles
– which she did. But then the other kids did as well, so
perhaps that's not such a big deal. Mind you, Andrea was the
first to go down with it.

I had to stop him telling his stories sometimes. I could see
the others were getting worried and I kept thinking he was
going to really come out with something – you know, like that
someone was going to die.

Janet had had a hard time though because the children
loved to hear Benedict's lurid tales – even while they were
scared stiff by them! 'One day at the end of school,' she said,
'he lingered and I asked him – joking, you know how you do,
if he had no home to go to. Then I noticed the poor little
blighter was in tears. I put my arm round him and asked him
what was wrong but that only seemed to make him worse.

He said, 'I love you, Miss Kelsey, but you're going to break
your arm and it makes me cry!'

I told him not to be so silly, but his words shook me, I can
tell you. He had that look in his eyes. It was uncanny – as if he
actually *saw* what he was telling you. He said, 'It's got to be
true: the Clock Man told me!'

I did break my arm a couple of weeks later, playing hockey.
Luckily it wasn't too bad, but I did have it in pot and
naturally, when I came to school like that, he reminded me:
'See, I did tell you. I was right wasn't I? The Clock Man is
always right.'

I'm only glad the children didn't hear that story. But I will
give Benedict his due on that score: he doesn't gossip, doesn't
try to make capital out of – what should we say? – his visitor.
He's quite unassuming really. And he *is* only a little boy. I was
touched when he said he loves me.

Janet had mentioned the incident to Benedict's parents.
'They laughed. They said he'd told them all sorts of things.
Nothing too bad – the shop fire in town was about the
worst.'

'And your arm.'

'And my arm. That wasn't too bad either. Anyhow, you
can't go blaming the messenger for the message, can you? It's
not his fault. He didn't *make* me break my arm.'

'The man in the clock has no face. Now that *is* eerie!'

'Don't you start! You're making me shiver.'

As we were leaving to go to assembly I stopped Benedict by the door. I said, 'I hear you're moving house and we shan't see you any more.'

He paused and looked at me as if I were a complete fool: 'Yes, I'm going to live in Bristol with Mummy and Daddy and I won't be coming to this school any more. But all the children will be leaving and going to another school soon: the Clock Man told me last night.'

I said, 'Will you see the Clock Man again?'

The disdainful look, only now he seemed to look relieved as well. 'No. There isn't a Clock Man in Bristol. I'm glad – because I don't like him any more.'

The following summer all the children in the old Infants and Juniors were moved to a new building. I suppose Benedict could have heard, or overheard, that this move was on the cards. On the other hand ...

7   Before the Event

Stephen and Jeanette Tomlison were so much in love that whenever they were seen together they brought a smile to people's faces. The Churchwarden said to me after the Parish Communion: 'They're like newly weds, Vicar. No – like teenagers out on a date!' Others said, 'They ought to grow up. It's embarrassing!'

I didn't find them embarrassing. What if they did hold hands in the Church Council meetings? It was damn friendlier, as a gesture, than shouting at one another, as some did. They might kiss now and again in public, but it was a fleeting smooch, a shuffle and a squeeze; nothing that would frighten the horses. In fact, they had the most perfect regard and consideration for each other. I would say that they were, for the brash inelegant twentieth century, a little demonstration of courtly love. I suppose that what made people smile was that they were in their fifties.

Stephen was Organization and Methods Co-ordinator for *Harland and Johnson (Metal Goods) Ltd*; 'What,' as he told me, 'they used to call "Time and Motion Study" before they became all hifalutin'.'

One day he tripped at work and hurt his back. I went to see him in hospital, 'Daft thing to do. I ought to have been more careful. But everything has to be so clean and polished, you'd think we were making baby food, not steel rivets. Anyway I slipped and here I am.'

'I expect Jeanette will be coming tonight?'

'She might. Well, she will, but she's bound to be late. She doesn't finish work herself until six o'clock and then it's a case of catching two buses.' His voice dropped as if he were beginning a conspiracy: 'She doesn't drive, you see. Not nowadays.'

47

A nurse arrived, looking as if she meant business, pushing a gleaming chromium trolley laden with sterile paraphernalia, so I excused myself. As I stepped out between the fire doors down the rubber walkway, Stephen's words came back to me: 'She doesn't drive. Not nowadays.'

Jeanette was not in church on the following Sunday, so, since I had to pass her house anyway on the way to the newsagent's, I called in. Usually so neat, today she looked crumpled, as if she was wearing someone else's clothes which were a bad fit. And her cheeks had that frosty look. 'Come in, will you?' There was no tone in the voice and this was odd because normally she had such an enthusiastic manner – even, as some said, gushing. She trudged from the hall to the sitting-room and flopped into an armchair.

'I'm done in.'

'Chasing off to the hospital every night?'

She lit a cigarette and the great cloud of smoke seemed to give her some comfort. It was like camouflage.

'I leave the library at six on the dot, Monday to Friday. Wednesday's half day. Well, there's no time to come home. It's a case of in to town and out.'

'Two buses?'

'That's right. And they're never on time. I'm fretting because I know I'm going to be late and Steve wants to see me. Well, I want to *be* there with him. Three-quarters of an hour in the ward – if that – and it's a question of stand and wait at the bus stop outside *The Florence Nightingale* – and there's always a queue – and then again in City Square. It's ten o'clock by the time I get home.

'And I worry, you see. I'm a born worrier. So I don't sleep. Many's the time I've been up at three o'clock making a pot of tea. Well – you end up like a wet rag.'

'Did you never drive?'

She gave me a wary look. 'What d'you mean "never"? Has Steve been talking to you? Did he tell you what happened?'

'He only said –'

'It was a long time ago, but it makes no difference how long: I'll never drive; not after what happened to me.'

Absentmindedly, she offered me a cigarette, and then, after I had refused it, she began to tap it on the polished table and stare at the wall, as if what she was remembering was projected there, like a film. She looked exhausted.

It was twenty years ago. Steve and I were living in Westerham, Kent. He worked at the paper mill in those days. We had some friends we used to see every Saturday in Tonbridge – well, one week we'd go to them and the next they'd come to us. Anyhow, this particular night it was their turn – their turn to have us over for supper, I mean.

I liked it. It meant I didn't have to cook and I always enjoyed the drive. Lovely country, Kent – d'you know it? Well, you want to make it your business to see it properly – that's in the springtime when everything's the freshest green and the bluebells are out in the wood on Ide Hill. I loved that drive.

I don't drink – never have done. So Steve would drive there, and I'd drive back. I like that, too. I liked the leaves of the trees in the headlights. It was like a fairytale – more so in those days before all this traffic.

We were coming back this particular night. It must have been about half-past eleven. We were never very late. Anyhow, we got to the top of Ide Hill – it's about two miles long, you know – and I switched off the engine as I usually did so we could freewheel and enjoy the silence. I kept touching the brake so it didn't run away with us. Just a nice, leisurely drive.

There was a big moon and it shone on the trees so that they looked wet and shiny on one side. Suddenly, I saw someone in the road – just standing there in the middle of the road with his arms out. A young man, no more than a lad really. He was in a sort of motorbike outfit.

I'd no time to stop. Of course I jammed on the brakes but I ran right over him: I know I did. It was terrible. I felt the back wheel go over his body. I screamed and pulled in to the side. We were turned half across the road and part pointing into the wood.

Steve – I remember his exact words – he said, 'What the bloody hell was that for?'

I was already out of the car and running back up the road. Steve came running after me, asking if I'd gone berserk. All I could say was, 'There's nobody here!' Again and again I repeated it, 'There's nobody here!' And there was nobody. Literally, no body.

I was crying and trying to make sense to Steve. 'I didn't see any young biker,' he said. 'It must have been a rabbit.'

Well, I was beside myself and I screamed at him that even I

knew the difference between a man and a rabbit. 'Where is he, then?' said Steve. Which was a good question because there was no sign of anybody, anywhere – not even a squashed rabbit.

I wouldn't go back to the car straightaway, but I combed that bit of Ide Hill in the moonlight. Nothing. No trace. And when we looked at the front of the car, there was no dent, no mark – nothing. And there ought to have been: it was one hell of a bump.

It must have been half an hour before I'd get back in the car and another half-hour before I'd let him set off. Steve was driving now. There was no way I was getting behind that wheel. When we got home, we sat up half the night and drank half a bottle of Scotch – a most unusual thing for me.

I could see the incident in detail – I still can. A clear stretch of road and then suddenly this figure looms up and I hit him. I saw what happened perfectly. He had a rucksack – the lad I knocked down – but it wasn't on his back. He was holding it on his arm as if getting ready to put it in a car that might be giving him a lift. It was flung a long way when we hit him.

Steve took me back to the exact spot in broad daylight. Still nothing. No rucksack. No mark on the road. Nothing. I was still wondering whether I should report it but Steve said, 'What d'you mean? What are you going to report – that you ran over the invisible man?'

I started to cry. I was in a bad way for days, and at nights I saw the scene again in my dreams: the young man, surprise on his face turning to terror when he realized I wasn't going to stop. Well, I couldn't. Then the rucksack sent flying and the back wheel going over the young man.

I'd wake up in a lather. Steve was marvellous. He was ever so patient. He'd give me a cuddle and make a pot of tea, and eventually I'd get back to sleep again.

It was wearing off, the whole experience, you know, fading. I'd just about convinced myself that it must have been some sort of hallucination. Steve said he reckoned I'd fallen asleep briefly and had a very vivid dream. That sounded right. I mean there was no trace of the lad, no report in the paper of anyone hurt – nothing. I was beginning to forget all about it. It was a dream and that was all there was to it. I'd convinced myself.

The chain-smoking, the fidgeting, the weary look. Jeanette was under a lot of stress, and I was starting to think that I wasn't making her any better by having her drag it all up again. But she insisted we have a cup of coffee. 'You don't know the half of it yet ...'

She sat in the big window with the light behind her, wisps of smoke rising from her silhouette. 'It was a month to the day. I opened the evening paper and nearly died of shock. There was a report: a young man in motorcycle gear had been knocked-down and killed by a hit-and-run driver. On Ide Hill at – as near as they could guess – about half-past eleven the previous night.

'They identified the poor devil but they never found out who did it. The lad was from Brighton. He'd been spending a few days with friends in South London, and they said he'd planned to hitch back to the south coast. God knows what he was doing so far off the beaten track.

'You can call me a coward if you like, but you won't get me behind a wheel again. I'm too scared of what I might see. I can't get away from the horrible idea that, because I *saw* what was going to happen, I somehow had a hand in causing it.

'Can you live with that?'

8   You'll be Free

Michael Thompson lived on the outskirts of Oldham, half-way up the Pennines, in a black stone house which looked down over Delph and Denshaw. He drove each day into Manchester, to his consulting rooms in Didsbury. He was a psychotherapist – the Jungian sort. He also wrote the 'A Doctor Advises' column in the evening paper. I wrote the Saturday religion column and so Michael and I met – I suppose it would be four or five times a year – at brainstorming or social gatherings arranged for us by the Editor. It was not always easy to tell which session was supposed to be for brainstorming and which for socializing.

Usually, we met in the newspaper offices, but in October 1984 we all converged on Michael's house at his kind invitation to supper after the meeting. It must have been on account of the proximity of Halloween – all provincial newspapers run a ghosts and ghoulies and things that go bump in the night piece in October – that, over the meal, we got to discussing the occult and the supernatural. All of us, that is, except John Denton, the Editor himself, who was far more interested in Michael's collection of Impressionist prints.

We were the usual crowd of local hacks. Elinor, the Women's Editor in her thick-framed glasses which certainly made a statement: 'Look at me! You will look at me, won't you?' Actually, she was rather wiser than the crop of the season radical-chic Women's Page Editor, though, it had to be said, – and it was Malcolm Bradbury who first said it – 'She dressed as if she was on her way to an erotic funeral.' Aromatic Elinor, full of chilled chablis and important issues.

Dave Laycock, the Travel Editor, always managed to give

the impression of being only half there. Not that he was at all lacking in the brainbox department, but he seemed to be perpetually on his way there and back. And he would regale anyone who cared to listen – and, indeed, anyone who did not so care – with his comparisons of standards of service on the world's airlines.

Keith Thornbury wrote sport and music and liked to think of himself as in the same league as Neville Cardus. Julian Coker was the TV critic. Three or four others had been invited but had sent their apologies for unavoidable absence.

As we ate, an autumn gale rattled the windows. 'Oh how charming – real shutters!' chirruped Elinor in a sort of stentorian squeak, as Michael got up to close out some of the noise. 'I should be terribly frightened if I lived up here on my own,' she said. But the idea of Elinor being anywhere on her own was a concept too difficult to entertain.

In the clattering semi-darkness we got to talking about Halloween. 'Of course, in Mexico they make a big thing of it you know,' said Dave. 'Not Halloween itself, but a couple of days after. They call it the Day of the Dead.'

Michael said, 'I wonder why people make more of Halloween – All Hallows Eve – than they make of the day whose Eve it is: All Saints? I don't want to believe it's because people are more interested in evil than in goodness; but I fear I'm right.'

John made a rare but, I thought, telling intervention when he said, 'Everything starts with evil, doesn't it? And everyone does. 'Course, you don't have to end there. But that's where you start, isn't it – in the darkness? What was it the alchemists said – you go for gold but you have to start with nigredo, black. Isn't that right, Professor?' He always addressed Michael as 'Professor'. Well, the man's appearance had 'Hollywood psychiatrist' written all over – it might have been in letters a foot high: small, dapper, white-haired, rimless glasses and an interrogatory voice which made him sound as if he was perpetually surprised.

Candlelight. Wine. Coffee and brandy. A succession of personal reminiscences on the seasonal theme. Everybody chipped in with their penn'orth: Keith even had a story about a ghostly cricketer who used to haunt the Stretford End at Old Trafford. Around the table, eyes shone with alcohol or credulity – or both. But it was Michael's story which really gripped the guests. It was an extraordinarily personal and candid story, and I doubt that it would ever have got told had it not been for the spiritual security which the brandy provided.

'Have you read the novel *She* by Rider Haggard?' he began. ' "She who must be obeyed." The enchantress or beautiful witch ...'

Elinor was not pleased at the route Michael's tale was taking: 'Isn't that all rather sexist, Michael? And old hat, too?'

He answered with an unexpected, because uncharacteristic, severity in his tone: 'I can't help it if it's sexist. It just happens to be the truth, that's all. And I can't help it if it's old hat either. I suppose the Bible and the *Iliad* are old hat – but that doesn't stop them from being interesting all the same.'

His seriousness made us all attend even more diligently. He went on, his voice softening as he came to describe the subject of his story.

'She was called Lucy. She was like one of the Sirens who tempted Ulysses' sailors off the isle of Capri. At any rate, she enchanted me. I met her in the dining-room of a small hotel after a day's walking on Pendle Hill ...'

'That's the witches' hill,' said Dave.

'As well it might be,' continued Michael. 'She was sitting at a table with an older lady, obviously her mother. Lucy: she had that apple-cheeked Englishness about her. A white dress with cuffs and a ribbon in her hair. Black hair. And I mean black. Nothing dark grey about Lucy.'

The psychologist Jung says that such beauties are personifications of the archetypal Anima, Goethe's *Ewig-Weibliche*, the Endless Woman Soul. The Helen of Troy sort. The face to launch a thousand ships. And utterly irresistible. Freud would say it's sexual attraction, pure and simple – or rather impure and complex!

For Jung it's more like demonic possession. He once wrote, 'When a respected septuagenarian runs off with a seventeen-year-old kitchen maid, we know the gods have claimed another victim.'

It was like that exactly with me – except I was only

thirty-two. It was adoration at first sight. I was utterly obsessed.

I knew I would just have to get to know her. I approached the two of them in the lounge afterwards. Nothing on earth could have prevented me. And I know I was talking drivel, jabbering like a confused schoolgirl. And, you know, they were so gracious.

He broke off and took another swig – swig, rather than sip – at the brandy glass. 'I shouldn't be telling you this. I feel a fool. But then I am – was – a fool!'

Heartfelt cries of, 'Oh, go on Michael!' So he did.

To cut a very long story fairly short at least, I got to know Lucy very well. She was a final-year music student at the Royal Northern College in Manchester – a singer. She played the piano rather well too. But her singing was the main thing. And when you heard her speak you didn't doubt it.

I was working with the Child Psychology Unit at the university at the time, so I got plenty of opportunity to walk the hundred yards along Oxford Road to hear her sing.

In time – not straightaway – but after a nervous start – the nerves were all mine – we became lovers.

Do you know anything about obsessive love? Do any of you? I meet it half-a-dozen times a year in my practice, but in those days I was a sufferer, a victim. I adored her. I danced around her. Friends were amused then appalled. Talk about making a fool of yourself! I was like the obsequious Basil Fawlty round the dining-table of a distinguished guest.

It was ecstatic and purgatorial by degrees. Manic-depressive, it changed by the minute. A real high-wire act. At times I knew – in my sensible moments – that it couldn't go on. No one can live like that permanently. But I couldn't live without her. Lucy filled my every thought. Lucy, like Lucifer, a bringer of light. The light of my life. I was a slave.

Our lives were music, poetry and travel. We had a week in Salzburg and Vienna for the Mozart Festival. It was as intoxicating as being actually in one of the Mozart operas. We spent glorious days in Cornwall and in the Scottish Highlands. We dined and danced and loved. Never such love!

And yet there were awfully bleak interludes. Just sometimes I would feel that everything was black, doomed. As if the enchantment oppressed me, took away my spirit and left me empty. She drained me. As Jung says, the glorious Anima also casts her Shadow.

We talked about marriage but – well, I don't know – I suppose I just knew we never would marry. One minute we were in heaven, on cloud nine. The next minute it was a hell of emptiness. I know now what it is – it's a kind of addiction. But then ... then, in those days, I was just enthralled – quite literally so.

When Michael began his story, one or two of us around the table chortled at what we saw as his romantic predicament. But as he progressed in the telling, I could feel the sympathy for him intensify. We fell strangely quiet and – as he had been – enthralled. There was a terrible sense of foreboding. At last it came ...

'We had rows,' he said. 'Horrible, demoniacal rows, passionate as love-making but infinitely dark. On those nights I felt I was looking into hell. After one such night we met for lunch the following day – in a little English tea-shop off Piccadilly.'

Lucy wore blue. She carried her little case of sheet music and her matching bag. I was dazzled by her. I began to make apologies about the previous evening's awfulness, but she silenced me with her smile and a shake of the head.

We sat at a table by the window, which was thickly glazed so that you could see the traffic but barely hear it. She ordered scrambled eggs on toast and I remember I ordered the same, though I can't recall eating the meal.

'Darling Michael,' she said. Her voice pure music. 'Darling, you know we must split up. And I know what you're feeling as I say this – please don't look at me like that! But this – our relationship – will kill you if we go on.'

'How can you say that? You're life and breath to me!'

'Yes, and death and torment,' she said. 'Look, you won't believe me now as I say this, but in time you'll see it's for the best. You'll extricate yourself. You'll be free. You'll thank me for this one day.'

I was struck dumb. I trembled. I felt sick. 'It's best,' she said. 'It's best we part. You'll see, in time. You'll be free, I tell you.'

Even the word 'part' was like a blade. I said I couldn't live without her, but she only smiled as she squeezed my hand. After a long silence she got up to go. 'No,' she said, 'don't come after me. You can't follow me – not this time.'

I watched as she went out of the door and across the street.

I lit a cigarette and ordered another cup of coffee. It was ten minutes to two and I was due at the hospital at half-past.

I couldn't go. I made an excuse and went out on the moors, walking. I got home about six o'clock and stared at the telephone, psyching myself up to ring her. Even as I gazed at the instrument, it rang. It was her mother, Lucy's mother. She could hardly speak. She began and then broke down. I could tell she was nerving herself. She sobbed. She said, 'I don't know how to break this to you. It's Lucy, I'm afraid she's gone ... she's dead. She was killed in a road accident at half-past eleven this morning. I tried to get you at work this afternoon, but they said you weren't in ...'

9 Apocalypse When?

'The RAF's response to the Russian Sputnik of 1957 was to send my dad out on the Yorkshire moors.' We were on a parish trip to Whitby, and Steve Rawson was coming across all creepy and nostalgic; but what he said was true.

The Yorkshire moors are a vast, natural park between York and the east coast. They are not mountainous – the highest point is not much above 800 feet – but they are dramatic and expansive: Beethoven country, you might say. They get more than their share of mist and drizzle but on a clear blue day you can see forever. From Fylingdales moor you can sometimes see Mount Ingleborough, forty-five miles away at the west end of the Dales.

Tourists charge across the moors in their cars, thinking that they are only passing through a wilderness – albeit a spectacular wilderness fractured by fleeting sunlight and aglow with a dozen shades of heather and wild blooms. But there is a secret world beneath the moors, 'in the dips' as the locals say. This is the world of a score of villages at the base of cliffs and hills so steep that clusters of houses and trees cannot be seen at all from the roads over the top. And so there are two climates: that of the austere, windblown moorland and that of these sheltered villages of proud houses in Yorkshire Stone set in green and gentle farmland. There can be a temperature difference of twenty degrees between 'the tops' and 'the dips'. The villagers know they are secluded and they want to keep it that way.

But to return to the Russian Sputnik and Steve Rawson's dad. The launch of the Soviet satellite showed how clever the Russians were at ballistics: if they could put a space capsule up there, they could also send up a capsule with an atomic bomb in it. What the West needed, therefore, was a very early warning radar system which would be able to track unfriendly missiles coming in from space.

Enter Alan Rawson. He was one of more than a hundred construction workers organized to build the early warning station for the RAF on Fylingdales moor. Within a very short time this was finished and it comprised the three 'giant's golf balls' which did service for thirty years before they were dismantled and replaced by more discreet, hi-tech equipment.

My dad and his mates saw all sorts out on that moor. You've got to imagine it – black as pitch at night and so exposed. There isn't a hill, you know, between the top of Fylingdales and Siberia ...

By now the whole coach was listening.

You have to remember the whole thing was supposed to be top secret. It was a mystery to the men themselves to begin with. Then they were all briefed one day. The Station Commander showed them a forces film about nuclear deterrence. It was still kept pretty quiet even after that, and you won't find any reference to the installation on the Ordnance Survey map.

After the briefing, when the whole thing was finished, the builders were given an official tour of the ops room. There was a hot line to 10 Downing Street and a scrambler – the lot.

At last it was time for all the construction workers to leave. Dad was with a group of lads who all came from York, and they were standing out on the moor waiting for the bus to take them home. Well, the bus had broken down just outside Pickering and it was getting late – about sunset. In July it was.

Most of the lads went back inside the compound for a drink and a game of cards while they waited for the bus, but my dad decided to walk down to the main road – about half a mile away – and hitch a lift in one of the cars coming back from a day trip to Whitby.

It was very open up there, exposed and a bit chilly even at that time of the year, so Dad didn't waste any time. He strode out towards the road. He could see somebody coming up from the road towards the compound. This was strange because all the personnel, RAF or civvies, came on the special buses or in their own cars. You had to have a pass in any case.

But this chap was walking, and it was obvious that his path

would cross with dad's. Anyhow, when he got up to him, the chap was wearing a strange uniform, like something out of the First World War. He nodded and smiled at my dad and asked him how long he had been working on the site, where was he off to now – that sort of thing.

My dad didn't say a lot. They'd all been told you couldn't be too careful. Then this chap in the old uniform said that war was a frightening thing. He knew, he said, because he'd seen a lot of it in one place and another. Then he said, 'This place you've been putting up: it'll all be taken down again and never used in anger. But what follows it – that will be used, I'm afraid!'

Dad was wondering what sort of clever dick he'd met up with but before he had a chance to ask him any questions, he just slapped him on the shoulder and walked past him up towards the base. My dad turned round to shout after him that there was no admittance to unauthorized personnel. But when he looked, there was no one there.

And there was nowhere he could have hidden. It was a straight path, half a mile over the open moor. So he walked back, my dad, all the way to the perimeter fence and asked the sentries if they had seen anyone. Nothing. Nobody had.

It is fifteen years since Steve told me that tale, and in the meantime the giant's golf balls have indeed been taken down, never having been used in anger. The stranger was right about that. But what about the second part of his prophecy? What about 'what follows it'? There it sits; a squat, white pyramid full of hi-tech electronics staring out into the changing sky that hangs over the moorland ... waiting.

10   No Wedding

Sigmund Freud outraged Victorian sensibilities by his ideas
about sex, sexual symbolism and infants' sexuality. In his
later works he stressed the relationship, as he saw it, between
the two most important, and certainly the most powerful,
instincts in human life: the sex-wish and the death-wish.
Freud did not merely pluck these ideas out of the air, but he
based them on evidence from the whole range and history of
western civilization.

Sex and death nearly always go together in the really big
human stories. The sin in the Garden of Eden myth was a
sexual sin, and its result was to bring death into the world.
When Ulysses was sailing back to Greece, he had to pass the
island of Circe, the witch. She and her beautiful colleagues,
the Sirens, sang to lure sailors with the promise of sexual
delights – only to dash their ships on the rocks. In the forests
of the Rhine, the Lorelei were said to do similarly with river
travellers.

In our own time, the horror movies frequently combine
sexual and ghostly elements. The evil Count Dracula, the
bloodsucker, is also portrayed as seductive. The very
expression 'femme fatale' makes explicit the theories of
Freud. While, according to Goethe, sex and death are
indispensable in a great novel or drama.

Our myths and stories are attractive to us because they
reveal hidden truths about our psychological makeup. They
ring true. We are fascinated and excited – haunted even – by
those erotic and ghostly tales. They answer to something
deep within us. According to Freud, they are projections, as
on to a screen, of psychological desires and fears within us,
within the unconscious mind.

The point about this sex and death connection is that it is real. The myths and fantasies are productions of what is actually going on within us. As another psychologist, the great C.G. Jung, said, 'Psychological events are really real.' And psychological processes have life and death consequences in daily living. I can recall one terrifying example ...

Martin was an accounts clerk who also sang in the church choir. He was in his early thirties and for years he had been – how shall I put it – the old phrase 'walking out' expresses it best – with Helen, age about twenty-five, who worked at the florist's. They held hands as they walked to church together and then he would take his place in the choir-stalls while she always sat in the same pew – half-way back on the south side directly under the second hymn-board.

Martin was huge but all his movements and gestures were gentle and unintimidating. He was shy: so retiring and biddable that you forgot his hugeness and tended to regard him as a vulnerable little boy. Everyone who got to know him did this. And he was an instant, furious blusher. A man of few words, he would always turn crimson when asked to say anything in public. Even when he initiated the conversation himself he would blush and his voice would come out in a hoarse whisper – as, for example, on the odd occasion when he volunteered his opinion about the phrasing of a verse of a Psalm in choir practice.

He was liked. People were affectionate about him and they tended to refer to him in his absence as 'poor old Martin' – but he wasn't poor and he wasn't old. You knew what they meant. A casual, friendly jest could throw him into a panic, and there were some in the parish who would rib him just for the effect. 'When are you and Helen going to get hitched, eh?' And you watched him dying of embarrassment.

Helen was very pretty, beautiful even, but this was not always immediately apparent. She dressed – well, not exactly dowdily, but conservatively. Nothing flashy or fashionable. Nothing that was particularly feminine. Not usually. But just occasionally she would wear something that demonstrated her prettiness, the usually concealed voluptuousness of her. I remember a yellow silk dress at a choir dinner. It startled everyone.

One January day, Martin and Helen came to the vicarage

and told me they would like to be married. She was quietly triumphant, even serene. He was obviously happy, but flustered beyond measure. He smiled – but at what cost! He had a crumpled piece of paper on which were written the hymns for the wedding, as if this were the most important and urgent aspect of preparation six months before the event! She filled in the necessary forms quickly and cheerfully. He wrote painstakingly, meticulously, as if engraving a roll of honour.

'Where are you going to live when you're married?' The word alone – 'married' – was enough to make Martin look up as if he had been shot. But Helen, all sunny, almost singing: 'We're staying in Leeds. In Farsley, in one of the new houses, top o' the hill – if it's ready in time.'

In the months that followed we had two more wedding interviews and the whole congregation was looking forward to the event. The ceremony was scheduled for the first Saturday in June, with a rehearsal booked for the Thursday before. As I explained to them, it was best to leave a full day between rehearsal and actual wedding to give time for any last-minute puzzlements about who says what and when to be gone over again if necessary. Besides, there was no good reason why the rehearsal should delay the commencement of the stag night. But, I reflected, stag night and Martin went together about as aptly as Pope and harem.

Helen's family regarded Martin very affectionately and jollied him through the business, future mother-in-law taking his arm and giving him a bit of a squeeze. His own parents were very obviously the blocks off which Martin was the substantial chip, and his father had the same vehement blush.

There was no wedding. On the Saturday morning at half-past eight, his mother found him still in bed, unconscious from an overdose of aspirin and paracetamol tablets. She said, 'I wondered how he could sleep so long on his big day. Knowing our Martin, I thought he'd be up and about at six out of nervous excitement. Anyhow, when it got past eight, I thought I'd waken him with a cup of tea ...' Her voice failed. Her eyes were sore.

I went to Helen's house at about eleven o'clock, as soon as I had come away from Martin's. He had been taken away by ambulance – the neighbours, having expected to turn out for

an altogether different sort of departure, were aghast and
agog. Helen and her folks were in the sitting-room, and the
atmosphere was like that which pervades when people are
waiting for the hearse. Endless cups of tea. Pointless
solicitations. Remarks made out of kindness and instantly
regretted for their banality. The room was all white and gold
and full of flowers. There was the smell of wine and cigars.
Helen, having just returned from the hairdresser, was in her
jeans. I said, 'I've been in touch with the hospital. He's going
to be all right.' No one said anything. Martin's father walked
out of the room and into the garden.

Martin did recover consciousness, but it would not be true
to say that he was ever all right again. In the weeks that
followed he hesitantly began to talk about what had driven
him to it. He told the same story, more or less, to the
psychiatrist and me.

'It was the nightmares. And then I realised they were more
than nightmares. *Nymphs and Shepherds* – that old song.
And they came, the nymphs. All in long, yellow silky things.
All night. I was possessed and polluted in my sleep. And then
even when I was awake in the night.

'I couldn't marry Helen after that ... filthy, ruined. I
couldn't contaminate her as well.' He had lost weight. He sat
in the wicker chair in his hospital room. He looked like a pile
of bones.

The psychiatrist had full notes of his interviews with
Martin: 'He was a virgin aged thirty-three. He adored Helen
but he had elevated her to the status of a goddess, pure,
untouchable. His desires had to go somewhere – I mean,
there was no doubt that Helen aroused him – so they went
into his dreams.'

That explanation is straight out of the modern textbook of
psychotherapy, and in detail it is littered with words such as
'repression', 'fixation' and 'unconscious motivation'. Earlier
centuries had another sort of explanaton which detailed the
same experiences. The medieval legends are of the sexy
visitors of the night who were thought to come and pollute
virgins. These seductive creatures – the Incubus and the
Succubus – were said to be from the Devil. Martin, as a
choirman, had often sung the ancient hymn at Compline for
deliverance from night terrors:

From all ill-dreams defend our eyes,
From nightly fears and fantasies;
Tread underfoot the ghostly foe,
That no pollution we may know ...

Nymphs and Shepherds? Well, that was a song the choir had sung at many a summer concert. And the yellow silk – Helen had a dress just like that. Hadn't she stunned everyone on that one occasion when she wore it?

Modern-minded people say, 'You can't believe all that medieval clap-trap about the Incubus and the Succubus!' But it seems to me that there is nothing to choose between the medieval doctrine and that of modern psychiatry, except a form of words. Both the old religious doctrine and the new scientific one describe the same experience. That is why the language of Incubus and Succubus made sense, horribly, to Martin.

The demons are beyond our conscious control: that is what the people of the middle ages believed. A scientific age, albeit based on the psychological mythology of Freud, speaks instead of 'unconscious forces'. These too are beyond our conscious control. It is simply a matter of terminology: our materialistic age prefers to account for its unknowns in scientific, or even pseudo-scientific, vocabulary. But Martin's experience would have been readily understood by a man from the fourteenth century.

Something, however you look at it, came by night and took away his innocence. He came out of hospital in due course and moved away. I left the parish the following year and, from what I have heard from old friends, Helen married a farmer and went to live in Skipton.

11 Another Country

For most people, ghosts are things that are seen by someone else, but now and again you come across a person who seems so at home in the world of spooks and strange visions that he appears almost to be on nodding terms with the supernatural. I know a man like that. For Geoff Horton, glimpses of the other world were no more unusual than a trip to the cinema.

He regularly saw his long-dead ancestors. They would slip in and out of Geoff's kitchen as if it was a coffee bar. 'Sometimes,' he said, 'I wake up in the night and my aunt Harriet – or it might be Uncle Ken – is standing by my bed. Nothing spooky about it at all. They're as real as you are.' It was unnerving to be accorded the same degree of reality as a ghost.

The ancestral shades were very well informed about worldly affairs: 'My grandfather, Herbert, on my mother's side, told me that Harold Wilson would lose the General Election which he called in 1970. "Too hot," said Herbert. "Too hot. He'll not get his people out to vote in June."

'And, you know, there was a heatwave and Harold lost.'

The ghosts also gave horse-racing tips and occasional selections for the football pools, but the lack of any major changes in Geoff's lifestyle suggested that his unearthly visitors were not as hot on economics as they obviously were on politics.

Geoff was not secretive about his visions, and he would pass on what he took to be useful advice, such as 'I wouldn't hold the church garden party in early July if I were you. We're in for a splash – that's what aunt Harriet says.' It was all said in such a matter-of-fact style, as if he had just watched the TV weather forecast.

He became well known for his acquaintance with 'the other side' and his nickname was Creepy Geoff – a misleading name really, for he was not at all creepy about his psychic experiences. Quite the reverse. He was so matter of fact and blasé about the whole thing that you felt the other world was scarcely less tedious and mundane than this one.

Geoff was in demand for his stories. I have seen the tap room in *The Myrtle* forget its clattering dominoes and beery gossip and fall silent, spellbound as Geoff told a new tale or even an old tale: 'I came out of the cemetery gates and realized someone was walking beside me. I wasn't frightened – no not one bit ...' But, in the clouds of cigarette smoke and yellow lights, you could tell that others were.

He once told me he had even seen one of my predecessors, a long departed Vicar of St Luke's. 'Had he come to find fault with my sermons, Geoff?'

'Oh no, not really. I was tending our Alice's grave one day and I heard this chortling. I turned round and he was standing by yon bench in bright sunlight. He said, "I see you're still having a devil of a time with the old church boiler!" '

Indeed we were. It was an old coke boiler which had to be lit on Saturday evening in order to warm the church for Sunday. Many is the time I have checked it was still lit at midnight only for the thing to be out in the early hours – usually on the wintriest mornings. A devil of a time we had with it, as Geoff and my predecessor's ghost remarked.

People were entertained by Geoff but no one took him seriously – largely because his ghostly predictions of fair or foul weather were about as reliable as his otherworldly racing-tips. 'Yes,' said Tom Shucksmith, 'it's all right your aunt Harriet saying that Golden Mile will win the St Leger, but does Golden Mile know it?'

One morning I called for my newspaper and someone in the shop said, 'Did you know old Geoff's ill?' I didn't, but I decided to drop in and see him that afternoon. Since Alice's death he had lived on his own, surrounded by his photographs. The walls of his house were like a picture gallery – but no, for I cannot imagine that any gallery would hang so many pictures so closely together.

To look at any one of Geoff's walls was like staring into a

crowd. And they all stared back, these familiar faces, framed or not, polaroid or sepia. I sometimes thought that Geoff's supernatural visions were no more than hallucinations brought on by his perpetual association with all those photographs. You did feel you were being watched. And the kitchen had a thousand eyes.

'It's my malaria, Vicar. I picked it up in the war in West Africa – white man's grave. It comes back now and then. Quinine – that's what we used to take, but I've got these new tablets now.' His face was shiny with perspiration and he made frequent use of his khaki handkerchief, but he was his usual cheerful self.

'Here, come and look at these books of mine. I've been wanting to show you them for ages.' He led me into the unused front room which smelled of camphor and in which the principal items of furniture were covered over with dust-sheets as if they had died. In the centre of the room there was a table covered by a green cloth and on it were piled a dozen or more bound books of the sort that are used for recording minutes of meetings.

'Come and look at this lot. I've never showed anybody else. See – I can go back years.' Dates and names written in copper plate handwriting and underlined in red. The precise times and details of spiritual encounters over decades, like the well-kept log from some ghost ship. 'Geoffrey, I'd no idea you kept such a meticulous record!'

He wheezed and perspired but he was pleased to receive my admiration. 'The first one, see, was my father. 1959 I believe it was. Yes, my old pa passed away in 1956. He'd just been and seen Jim Laker take nineteen wickets against the Aussies at Old Trafford.'

It was a brief entry and, to be honest, as banal as anything you might receive from a seaside fortune-teller and to the effect that Geoff (according to Pa) would never be rich, but he would never be poor either; and he must take care of Alice. 'I always did take care of her,' said Geoff now, his shiny face turning even more pink and his eyes taking on a distant look as if he himself had begun to drift into the past, 'she was the light of my life and I loved every hair of her head.'

I leafed through the gold-edged pages. Here they all were,

the names regularly recalled before the *Myrtle* regulars. Harriet and Emily and George and one or two names from the last century including Sir Edward Brancepeth who had fought in the Crimea. Shirley Partridge, the greengrocer's wife who had died the previous March, had also put in an early appearance; but it was only to give a smattering of gratuitous advice about throat lozenges.

'Now, Vicar, my problem is I've no one to leave this lot to – Alice and me never having any family. And I wondered if you'd like 'em?'

I must say I felt like the Scottish Presbyterian who had just been presented with a gross of rosaries. I said, 'That's generous of you, Geoff. I'm honoured.'

'You know about such things – being a parson. I wouldn't want them going to just anybody. I see my work, keeping a proper record, like doing local history. All the folks in those books lived in these parts. What they had to say – what I wrote down – well, it'll add a bit to general knowledge, eh?'

He went to the largest dust-sheet, fumbled with it and brought out a bottle of rum. Soon the house was filled with an aroma which even overwhelmed the camphor. 'You like a drop of spirits, Vicar?' I stifled an attack of the giggles.

He coughed uproariously and then said, 'I'm not afraid of dying you know. There's nothing to be afraid of. The way I see it is that this world and the next are just like two countries that share a border. I reckon I'm privileged. Everyone can't live on the border, but I do. And so, naturally, I sometimes get visitors from the other side. One day I'll go and join them, and I shan't need a passport.'

He stared down into the glass of brown liquid, and for the first time I realized that he was an old man. The busyness, the chirpiness and his enthusiasm for what I suppose was his supernatural hobby usually combined to make him seem much younger than his seventy-nine years. But the malaria had knocked the stuffing out of him and for once he looked his age. He had a full head of fine white hair and bright blue eyes. His complexion was weather-beaten and wrinkled – an angelic face, well lived in. He sipped the rum and I could tell he was having difficulty with his breathing. I looked back at the books. Anyone might have taken them for stamp albums.

'You see, Vicar, I think these books of mine might do

people some good – in your hands, I mean. You could use them to teach people that there's no need to be afraid of dying. "Grim Reaper" and all that – it's not right. It's not true. Death is our friend, and dying is only like visiting that other country.'

' "Our sister death", St Francis said.'

'Did he now? Well he must have known a thing or two. And I shall see Alice again. I know because she's told me.'

The attack of malaria had been masking a worse illness – pneumonia. He died a fortnight later, sitting in his chair by the open window. Denis Backhouse the undertaker phoned me, and I went round to Geoff's house. He looked to be at peace. The only sound was of birdsong in the drowsy heat.

A few weeks later I took delivery of his notebooks and turned the pages to discover his last entry. It said, in the same copper plate, 'Darling Alice visited me. She said all was well and that she would see me very soon. She said that this would be her last visit and that now it was my turn to visit her. And it would be just like the old times only more so. "God bless you, Geoffrey!" she said. "I'll be waiting for you".'

The account ended there. It was dated three days before he died.

12   Father

In the County Arcade in the middle of Leeds, there is a world-famous toy shop. Years ago there was a dolls' house in the window, a fixture which everyone came to see. There were crinoline and old lace figures in it which moved by a mechanism that looked like magic. They wore weird smiles, these mechanical dolls, and there was an unearthly aspect about them which frightened the children. Frightened but fascinated: you could see it all in their faces pressed up against the glass.

I knew two women who were like those dolls. Not weird sisters, but mother and daughter. They lived – though 'lived' is a word that sounds like an exaggeration – at the end of a country lane on the outskirts of Leeds where I worked as Curate at the Parish Church. Children did not peer in at the window of these two ladies. In fact, some children said they were witches and made up rhymes about them which they would chant and then run away.

Sylvia and her daughter Lilian. They had not always lived alone. Once there was 'father', but he had died, as the *Yorkshire Post* said, 'after a long illness borne with great fortitude.' That was Sylvia's wording: Sylvia with her fine hair drawn tightly back off her forehead; Sylvia who had been born in the nineteenth century and who still lived in it.

Lilian was fortyish, but of the sort who probably looked fortyish at the age of sixteen and who would look the same aged seventy. She moved noiselessly but this only intensified her presence. Lilian with the porcelain complexion and the bright blue eyes – like a doll, you might say. It did not occur to you to wonder that she had never married, even though she was breathlessly sexy. Heavy breasts on that delicate, slight frame went with a voice that any PR company switchboard would have paid a million pounds for.

She did not work as a telephonist or indeed at anything else except 'looking after mummy'. Mummy was in the most robust health and yet, like a rich old tyrant in roles played by Bette Davis, she needed to be looked after. So Lilian stayed at home. There was no shortage of money. Father had been 'well-placed' on the board of Turner's Furnishings and Fittings, and he had owned a score of properties in the Headingley area which were let to university students and young professional people. When he became 'a sick man' his wife and daughter looked after him so assiduously that malicious locals claimed that really they were poisoning him systematically. That Bette Davis film atmosphere hung about the place.

They used to bring him, glazed-eyed, to church in his wheelchair and a space was made for him at the front. He could not kneel, of course, and so taking the sacrament to him involved a little procession by one of the clergy. This had gone on for so long that churchgoers regarded it as part of the liturgy. The women always pushed the wheelchair holding a handle apiece, like teenagers proud of a new baby. All their movements were so precise and predictable that they were remarked on and became comic. The way they manoeuvred the lychgate. The way they walked arm in arm to their pew after they had delivered father to his place. These movements became ritual alongside their churchly ritual gestures, which they performed symmetrically so that again the effect was comic. Two signs of the Cross. Two exquisitely choreographed genuflexions. Two heads held at the exactly similar and slightly exaggerated angle to receive the bread and wine. They were a liturgical *pas de deux*, or as Emily Hoskins put it, 'It's like they're doing the hokey cokey.'

Father's illness had not affected his speech, yet the women spoke for him as if he had been struck dumb. 'Father's a little bit brighter today' or 'He had a bad night, didn't you, Father?' Always spoken a little more loudly than ordinary speech and more pointedly as well, as if the old man's intellectual faculties had been wasted by his disease.

When he became too ill to attend church, I took Holy Communion to the house every Wednesday morning. It was like a military exercise – church parade. Everything was so precisely ordered. The women always set out the little table and spread over it a linen cloth exquisite as a Victorian christening robe. They struck the match to light the candles as soon as I was inside the door. A quarter-slice of fresh white bread was placed on the silver plate. No one spoke, but Lilian always smiled a distant smile like a lesson in dramatic irony. The precisely regulated actions were those of women going through the motions.

After the short service, father would nod and cough his gratitude, while Sylvia said 'Thank you' as she placed with great emphasis a fifty-pence coin on the corner of the little table. Lilian had already removed the candles and almost at once she would return with the tray bearing the coffee pot and three cups and saucers. 'Father never bothers with a drink mid-morning, do you, Father?' Three shortbread biscuits.

Lilian would glide about the room, repositioning small ornaments. Father, his complexion yellowing by the week, would struggle with his breathing to make conversation. He knew only one topic: the state of the property market. This routine continued for about six months until, one night, I picked up the phone to hear Lilian's canorous accent telling me that Father had 'passed away'. That was the beginning of the strangeness.

When I went round to the house the following morning, I was told that Father had given strict instructions that he did not want a funeral service of any kind but simply, as Sylvia said, 'to be taken straight to the crematorium and disposed of. No words. No fuss.'

'But he was always such a churchman. The house Communions ...'

'That's what his instructions were.' She interrupted me with what were clearly intended as her last words on the subject.

A week later, the minimalist funeral over and done with, I went round to the house again. The same quietness and preciseness but no table set out for Communion and no Lilian. 'She's gone into Leeds to attend to some of father's business papers. Well, I would have gone but I'm so slow these days I would only have held her up. Will you have some tea?'

'You were both very good to him. You must miss him now he's gone.'

'Just sit down there and let me tell you a few things. You don't know a half or a quarter of it.'

It all came out. 'You never knew father – not like I knew him, like Lilian knew him. I couldn't begin to tell you …' (It did not prevent her) '… how he treated us. You only knew him as a sick man, in that chair. But he wasn't always like that, Oh no. He was cruel, mean. He kept me on a tight leash from the day we were married. That fifty pence we used to give you when you brought Communion. It was embarrassing but it was all he allowed. He insisted upon it.

'And he could be violent. He beat me, before and after Lilian was born. He used to go off to a peculiar place in Leeds – near where he owned his old houses. I hated it when he went there because when he came back I knew he'd lash out at me. He did some awful things to me. He would shout and bawl and call me a whore … and force me to do things.'

'Why did you never say anything?'

'What *could* I say? I was ashamed. Afraid and ashamed. And I had Lilian to think about. It wasn't long before he started on her. He would threaten me and send me out but I could hear him from the bedroom. He called her "Father's little girl" – the times I've heard her whimpering and crying. And he said Father's girl was never going to get married, never going to leave him. Because, as he said, he loved her. Loved her! It makes me sick to think about it.'

'I wish I'd known about all this.'

'Nobody knew. We told nobody. You've no idea the things that man did to us.' The woman began to cry. I went to put my arm around her shoulder and she recoiled, panic-stricken, her eyes boiling with tears and anger. There was a sound and Lilian came in. She looked, then looked away bewildered, the porcelain complexion reddening. 'So, you've told him everything!'

'I've only told him what was true, darling.'

'I'll bet she hasn't told you the half. I'll bet she hasn't told you about the rows – rows between me and my dear mother because she accused me of encouraging him!' This was a vehement, turbulent side of Lilian I had never seen before.

'Oh, I didn't mean it, darling. You know that. I was just so upset I didn't know what I was saying sometimes!'

Lilian went and held her and they became calm. 'It's so shameful. So embarrassing.'

'There's no need to be ashamed,' I said, 'or embarrassed. Look, this is going to take some time getting used to, but it's all over now – really it is. You can start to put it behind you, get better. I'll help you.'

'There's no one can help us.' The old lady looked fierce – fierce yet calm like one driven past long endurance. Her daughter held her hand, and the two of them seemed to concur in an awful silence.

Then Lilian said, 'I used to say to him that I didn't know how he could behave as he did and take the Sacrament. He said he took the Sacrament to show his contempt for it – and for us.

'The really terrible thing is that we're not free of him. We're not now and we shall never be.'

'He's dead, Lilian.'

'Is he? And without a funeral. He used to promise that he'd come back and take us to him, one at a time as he saw fit and when we least expected it.'

'That was just to frighten you. It was a wicked thing to say. But you really must put it out of your mind now. He can do you no more harm. You're safe. Let me try to help you, please – as a friend and as your priest.'

'What was it he used to say, Mother? Priests – "scum on the pond".'

There was a long pause. The tea was undrunk. It was raining hard and the garden was under a mist. There was a sound from upstairs, as of one making a sudden movement, an effort as it might be to get up out of bed with difficulty. The women looked at each other.

'Near the university, where he used to go,' said Lilian, 'there was a horrible bookshop that sold books about black magic. I knew he went there. Some people I know saw him. And those who kept the bookshop – they did things …'

'Please try not to think about all those things now. Look, I'm going to ask Dr Drury to call on you –'

'We're not crazy, you know!'

'Of course you're not crazy! But you've been through an ordeal. It wouldn't do any harm to –'

'He's already been. There are two bottles of pills in the bathroom chest: one blue and one yellow, one for her and one for me.' There was a strange look on Sylvia's face, half-way between mockery and hysteria. They had had enough talking for one day. I said I would call again soon, then made my way out into the summer rain.

I did call again. I called each week for several months and observed a change in the women that was like a resurrection from the dead. The house was redecorated top to bottom, inside and out. There was music playing from the radio. The two women seemed like two distinct individuals instead of that cramped, fugitive duet. They no longer seemed haunted.

After carol singing around the suburb one night, Sylvia asked me back to the house for a drink, and it was there that they gave me the news. Lilian had taken a part-time job in the local library and she had become engaged to one of her colleagues there. The world had seemed to change from black and grey into glorious technicolour.

Early in the New Year, Lilian was knocked down in the middle of Leeds and killed. There was a witness who told the police, 'I've never seen anything like it. She just walked straight into the traffic – never looked this way or that.'

Sylvia reverted to her former silence and fell into a decline from which she never recovered. She died six months later, it was said from a combination of problems with her heart and liver. More heart than liver, I would have said if anyone had asked me. A week before she died, I visited her in the Brotherton Wing of the Leeds General Infirmary.

She was hooked up to tubes and gadgets. Her face was a grey hollow and her various treatments had made her almost bald. She whispered to me: 'It was Father. He came to me the night Lilian was killed. You remember that noise we once heard from upstairs? Well, that again. It was him. I saw nothing but I heard him, no mistake.

'He said, "She's here with me now, our Lilian. And you won't be long!" '

At the beginning of the autumn term, I happened to be at the philosophy department in the university. I enquired about the bookshop which allegedly supplied the black magic literature. I was told that it was all boarded up. Apparently it was always being raided by the police – not on account of the books about Satanism but because of the hard Left political stuff which they were said to stock and because the proprietors had been caught receiving a huge supply of drugs.

No one could tell me anything about 'Father', but the Secretary to the department said, 'All kinds of odd characters used to hang out around there. I felt spooky just walking past.'

13   Domestic Miracle

Not all supernatural stories involve ghosts, but some involved miracles. I think I have observed a miracle.

James Sugden and his wife kept the newsagent's shop on Wellington Road in Leeds. Their daughter, Pam, married Dennis Hanley, who was a salesman with a furniture company in Headingley. They had a child, Caroline. I got to know Caroline almost as soon as she was born. It was a difficult birth and she had almost choked on the umbilical cord and, whether or not this was a cause of future difficulties, she grew up beset by nervous, emotional problems.

Perhaps because Caroline had had a narrow escape, her parents always treated her as if they might lose her at any moment. They pampered her and indulged her until she became surly and dissatisfied. When it was time for her to go to school there were tantrums, and Dennis and Pam often had to go and talk to the class teacher.

She misbehaved in Sunday School as well. 'Attention seeking, that's what it is. She's a proper little madam, that one!' said Molly Grant who had charge of Caroline's group. Then she developed a nervous cough and suffered nightmares. She missed time at school, and when she had been away from school it was difficult to get her to want to go back.

The one person in the world who seemed always to be able to coax the best out of Caroline was Grandad James: 'Grandad Jim', as she called him. He had, as he said, once ... 'And *only* once told her straight what sort of behaviour would be tolerated and what not.' She – the manic, never stay in one position for two minutes at a stretch jack-in-the-box –

would sit on her grandad's knee for half an hour or more while he read to her or told her what she referred to as 'one of your made-up stories.' The child had two natures: the irascible, unbiddable aspect which she presented to the world, sticking her tongue out, and the gentle, even serene, character which she became when Grandad was around.

When Caroline was about seven, Dennis was made redundant by the furniture company and the family was plunged into crisis. They were rescued by James who declared himself too old to run the newsagent's business by himself and so appointed Dennis as manager. It had seemed to be a fortuitous move because no sooner had Dennis got to know the ropes than James' bronchitis worsened and he had to give up working altogether. Dennis took over full charge of the shop, while his parents-in-law entered into their retirement, letting it be known that they would be on hand to smooth out any difficulties which might be encountered by the willing but inexperienced young manager.

At about this time Caroline developed psoriasis. The flaky rash covered her arms and legs, and she was teased at school. Her behaviour worsened, and in the end she had to leave and go instead to a Special School for children who were emotionally disturbed.

Unaccountably, the newsagent's business went into decline. It had always done so well and it was regarded locally as 'a gold mine'. Old James Sugden and the missus had kept open all hours and people got to rely on the place for emergency supplies. If your living-room light-bulb blew at ten in the evening, you could always run round to 'Jim's' and get a replacement. Shoelaces, sticking plaster, buttons and studs, cigarettes, disposable razors, greaseproof bags, batteries for the radio – all the trappings of hand-to-mouth bourgeois survival were stocked somewhere behind that door through which there seemed always to ooze a trickle of light whatever the hour.

The old couple were perplexed by the sharp reduction in the shop's takings; and more than perplexed for it was, after all, their lives' work. James was very ill by this time, and he was being hauled off to Leeds General Infirmary for tests. It is remarkable how many different reasons a parson can list for visiting a particular family, especially a troubled family. I had been a close observer of Caroline's problems since her birth. There was the problem of Dennis' redundancy which, taken with the anxiety about their daughter, had upset relations between Dennis and Pam themselves. But my most urgent reason to call on them was James' illness. It was November when I saw him and just after the hospital tests. He was sitting by the window watching the rain as I walked up the drive.

They had found a tumour on his lung and they were going to operate. 'It's not that that worries me, though.' He spoke calmly but his face was sombre. He looked like a disappointed man. 'We've had our troubles, but it's the very devil when you can't trust your own.' He did not say any more at the time, except a mumbled phrase about 'funny goings on at t'shop.'

They did operate and they sent him home to convalesce. I went to see him once or twice and he seemed resigned. His wife hardly spoke. She walked slowly, bringing in tea and scones, attentive to James' needs but giving nothing away about the issue – whatever it was – with which she was clearly preoccupied.

Just into the New Year she came to the Vicarage at about half-past eight one evening. She clasped her hands in front of her. She was white, shaking. I imagined that James had taken a turn for the worse. 'It's not just James,' she said. 'It's the whole family.'

I sat her in front of the fire and gave her a brandy. 'He's known all along – about Dennis, fiddling the till and the books. Then our Pam came and admitted it. She'd caught Dennis at it – they were in debt, you see. Dennis had been used to a bit of style when he was in the furniture business and he never got used to having to draw his horns in.

'James hit the ceiling when she told us, but – he's as soft as putty – he said he'd let Dennis off. He'd forget about the money and trust him to run a clean ship in future. Then Dennis got mad with Pam for owning up on his account, and I'm afraid he hit her ...'

She knocked over the brandy glass and gave in to her tears.

When she had recovered, she said, 'Dennis won't even see Father. He's stopped looking after the shop – Pam and I have been trying to keep it going between the two of us. But then there's Caroline to worry about, and she takes some minding, believe me.

'On top of it all, they've found another tumour in James' other lung and they're going to operate again. He's convinced it'll be the finish of him. I know the shop has to be kept going, but my husband needs caring for as well; and I've only got one pair of hands ...' She was wringing her hands, trembling beyond control.

I said I would go and see Dennis and Pam. My idea was to get him to understand the seriousness of James' illness. I was sure that would be the best way to rally the whole family.

'He'll know I've told you.'

'Not if I call to talk about his father-in-law.'

'It won't do any good.'

I tried nevertheless. And it did not do any good. Dennis was guarded, surly, and he more or less told me to mind my own business. To make matters worse, he had forbidden Caroline to go and see her grandad. That was silly rather than cruel, and I was sure Dennis was acting out of his own guilty feelings. Caroline's psoriasis was worse. Somehow Pam and her mother managed to keep the shop going, but everyone said it was going downhill. You couldn't get the things you wanted. And they shut at six sharp. Pam was not very good at supervising the newspaper delivery lads.

James had his second operation in May and now he needed an oxygen mask for part of each day. He said the nights were horrible. He sat for hours behind the plastic mask, wheezing, his eyes moist and bulging. He told me he hardly had the strength to read the paper some days – this from a man who used to deliver two sacks of them seven days a week. But he worried most because he did not get to see Caroline.

'I don't bear Dennis any grudge. Who knows what any of us would do in the same circumstances – but I wish he'd let the little girl come and see me. Maybe it's best she doesn't see her grandad like this.'

He was like a man resigned – or rather like a man who would be quite happily resigned if he could have his one wish. He loved that little tartar.

Three weeks later James died at home, peacefully. I saw him the day before he died, but he could not talk much and he was in and out of sleep. But he was at ease with himself.

His wife told me, when we were alone downstairs. 'He's happy enough now. Caroline came to see him yesterday. He hadn't the breath to read but, d'you know, she read to him. She was ever such a good girl.'

About a fortnight after that I went in the newsagent's shop and Dennis was behind the counter. Suddenly Caroline emerged from the living-room in a smart school uniform and ran out of the shop door to catch the bus. She smiled at me as she ran by. She looked well ... friendly.

Dennis smiled at me as well but I could see that he was fighting back the tears. 'You don't know the half of it, Vicar. What a fool I've been. So bloody selfish. That girl went to see her grandad – I was wicked to try and stop her – and the old man put his hands on her head and blessed her. She told me herself. He said, "Bless you my little love! You'll be all right now."

'The day Jim died, I looked at Caroline and there wasn't a trace of psoriasis on her. Of course I took her to the clinic and they said it sometimes does clear up spontaneously. But I know different. We all know different now.'

14 Near Death Experience

Three people have told me of their 'near death' experiences. Two of these accounts are interesting, but the third is something else altogether.

The first concerned a wealthy man who lived in a manor house. He was in his sixties when he developed incurable cancer. Being a plain-speaking and courageous man, Michael asked the specialist to tell him straight away how long he had to live. 'But, Peter,' Michael told me later, 'I wasn't at all prepared for what he said. I thought he would say I'd got a few years – time, you know, to adjust, put my house in order. He said, "Are you sure you want to know?"

'Well, I ought to have expected something nasty there and then, didn't I? "Three months, Michael," he said. "Three months." Just like that. That was all.'

The master bedroom in the manor looked out over well-kept fields and woodland. There was a magnificent lake which acted as a mirror for the poplars and, in the autumn, the whole effect was like an Impressionist painting. Michael was usually in his dressing-gown, sitting up in bed or in the wicker chair by the window. He was above medium height, elegant and handsome in the style of the jolly decent fellow in old black and white films about the minor aristocracy.

I would go and sit with him for an afternoon each week. He liked poetry – reading it out loud or quoting from memory. And music. He loved to point out aspects of the landscape which I had not noticed. And then he would simply tell me, out of the blue, little facts about his milieu, as if making presents of bits of his life: 'You know, under our kitchen, there's an ice house. Amazing how they learned to preserve ice even before refrigerators, eh?'

Michael also talked abut God and the life of the world to come. He was a solid, unemphatic Christian gentleman who had imbibed the doctrines of the faith, as it were with his mother's milk. It never occurred to him to doubt his beliefs, but neither did he harp on them in that over-confident style which always makes me suspect insecurity if not insincerity. But he developed a little – only a little – more pressing interest in his everlasting fate as he stood on the threshold of it. He said, 'I haven't been a saint, Vicar. But I trust God to look after me.' As good a confession of confidence as I could wish to hear.

One Friday afternoon I called to see him and his wife, Marion, forewarned me: 'You'll wonder what's got into Michael. He's sort of euphoric. He's had this dream – he says it was more than a dream. It's all he can talk about. Anyhow, he'll tell you himself. I'm just pleased if he's been given a bit of comfort, consolation.'

He was exultant. 'Come in, Peter. Come in! There's nothing you or anyone else can tell me about heaven now. Even the Archbishop of Canterbury couldn't tell me anything now. I've seen for myself.

'You'll say it was a dream, but it was more than a dream: it was a foretaste. In fact that was exactly what the angel said. But look, sit down and I'll start at the beginning …'

And it all came out in excited gasps. He spoke in the enthralled style of a child recounting a fairytale which, however, was no fairytale to him but pure magic.

I was in the garden. I thought I really *was* in the garden. It was high summer and the beds were ablaze with flowers. It was a cloudless day, like a childhood memory. I was sitting out in my usual chair under the willow, and I remember I had no pain. I was just thinking how good it was to be in no pain when the angel appeared....

Yes, an angel. A real angel. White and gold like an Italian painting. There was music but I couldn't tell where it was coming from. He said, 'Come with me!'

I followed him into the orchard and along the path where the little stone statues are. Then I saw him. I remembered straightaway the words in the gospel about Mary at the resurrection: 'And she, supposing him to be the gardener.' That's who I thought it was at first. And then I realized. It was him. He was standing there, smiling, with his arms held out. He didn't say anything but I was suddenly filled with the sense that everything was all right. I had this conviction that the whole of my life had been worth it – all the pain, all the difficulties. That everything had been leading up to this moment – seeing him there – which put everything else into perspective.

I ran towards him but that was when the angel held me back and said, 'Not now, Michael. But this is a foretaste, to encourage you and to help you.'

I woke up. I told you, you'll say it's a dream. It didn't feel like a dream. But perhaps it was. God does speak through dreams sometimes, doesn't he? I mean in the Bible?

Dream or not, the encouragement worked for Michael and he died ... I can only say serenely. But he did not merely die well: the last few months of his life were lit with a secret light and he was a delight to be with. He instructed that the church be decked throughout with white flowers for his funeral and that the resurrection story should be read in place of the usual lesson.

Not Michael alone, but Marion too drew strength from the visionary experience, and she told me many times in the weeks that followed how consoled she was by what had happened. 'I feel the encouragement was for me as well,' she said.

The second near-death experience recounted to me was that of an old lady, Agnes, who had sung in the church choir for fifty years and, as she liked to remind me, 'With the Leeds Philharmonic when Leonard Bernstein came and we sang Mahler's *Eighth*.'

Mahler's *Eighth* Symphony ends with a vision of heaven expressed musically by huge choirs, soloists and a vast orchestra. No wonder that its nickname is *Symphony of a Thousand*. Agnes, radiant, said, 'It was just like that. I must have seen the same vision as Mahler. I, all of us, was being taken up into God's loving-kindness.'

The experience had happened while her heart was stopped.

She was resuscitated with all the usual commotion, but she died two days later. She had asked for Holy Communion and, after receiving it, her last words to me were, 'I have no fear. My mind is at rest.'

Michael and Agnes were believers, but the most remarkable of the near death experiences was told to me by Alan, a convinced atheist. He was not the calculating, mechanical sort of atheist – the kind whose religious opinions are more like accountancy than divinity – but a large, cheerful pagan who took too much pleasure in the good things of this world to spend much time worrying about the next.

He was a schoolteacher – boys' PE. That was only the start of it. Out of school hours he ran about half-a-dozen cricket and football teams and, when there were no matches to be played, he was off with troops of young lads tramping the Lake District hills or the Yorkshire Moors. He was like a big ginger bear with a sweetshop smile. But when he was forty-one he developed leukaemia.

They treated him partly with transfusions and, in the few days after each new intake of blood, he showed signs of his old energetic self, only to lapse before long into his weakened and deteriorating state. It was pitiful to see such an outward-bound man so miserably confined.

It's strange: you think you know all there is to know about a character and then he goes and springs a massive surprise. Alan, I would have said, was not at all the reflective type. Not that he was unintelligent or insensitive, but reflection requires moments of stillness, and, until he fell ill, I never saw Alan still for five minutes in my life. But I went to see him in the Leeds General Infirmary and he was sitting up in bed reading Immanuel Kant's *Critique of Pure Reason*.

He acknowledged my stupefied look with a grin. 'Yes, well, now I can't get about, it's time I used a bit of mental muscle. It's not entirely new to me. When I was at university I read Philosophy as a subsid, two years out of the three. You'll be surprised to know I got a distinction at the end of Part One.

'I took up philosophy because my grandfather recommended it. He was the cleverest man in the world. He told me straight, "Tha might break thi back. So get some wisdom as well as brawn. Tha dunt want to be known as t'lad who's strong i't'back and weak i't'ead."

'So I took up Philosophy. Liked it as well — much to my surprise.'

The old ginger bear was thinner these days. He read his Kant and he asked me for additional books and commentaries, but he showed no inclination to talk about what he was reading. He seemed to have the same attitude towards Philosophy as he had towards his sport: you just got on with it.

The appalling disease brought him low, and I was called to the ward one morning to be told that in the night he had all but died. 'We had a platoon of medics round his bed at half-past midnight,' said the Staff Nurse.

He was lying there in a hospital gown, propped up on two or three pillows. He had gone almost to a shadow. His cheeks were like grey caverns, and he was bald as a result of his many treatments. I sat at the bedside, and he began to speak quietly. His voice was all astonishment, but somehow also calm. He wanted very much to tell me something, as he put it, 'now'.

You know when you're training? You get fit. If you get superfit, you can run a mile in four minutes. Maybe you could even run a mile in three minutes. But you could never run a mile in, say, eight seconds — however fit you were. That's impossible. It's just something *beyond*.

It's like that in Kant. I've been thinking about it. You know, Kant says all that we experience are phenomena, but there's another sort of thing we can't experience and he calls them noumena. The noumena are beyond us — like an eight seconds mile is beyond us.

God is beyond in this sense, according to Kant. Well, I'd read that stuff when I was in college and I dismissed it. What's the point in trying to talk about what's beyond what you can talk about? It's a waste of time. Might as well try to run an eight seconds mile. Can't be done.

Last night, when they were banging my chest and shoving all kinds of needles in me, I was in a dream. No, it wasn't a dream. I was in a little town, Konigsberg. Kant's city. I knew it was. Then suddenly there he was too — coming out of a coffee house. There was a clock and it said half-past eleven.

I spoke to him. I said, 'Where am I, sir?'

And he said, 'You're among the noumena, young man. In fact you're becoming one of the noumena yourself.'

It sounded so silly and I felt embarrassed. And then slowly I started to become aware of things as I'd never known them before. The sign outside the coffee house. The watch I was wearing. The sounds of the city ... I was hearing and seeing them for the first time. I was seeing them as they are in themselves.

And then Kant himself was telling me: 'These are the Things in Themselves, Alan. You can see them as they really are because for the first time you are as you really are.'

You were there too, Peter. And my grandfather and all my family. And the schoolboys I go walking with. All the boys I've ever gone walking with. There was nothing strange about it. You know, what's strange is *this*, where we are now. The world – it looks odd, incomplete. It's like when you've got a radio on and it's only half tuned in. Like when you can't make out someone's face in the dark.

But *there*, in noumena land with Mr Kant. It was real. Really real. I don't suddenly believe something now that I didn't believe before. I haven't seen anything different. I've just seen things as they are. You know, now I want to go back there.

He died within the week. During his last few days he spoke again about his experience. He kept saying there was nothing weird about his vision. His last words seem to me utterly remarkable, so down to earth and unsensational – just like Alan himself – but so solid and intensely memorable that for me they have the ring of truth.

'Kant told me: "This, where you are now, isn't out of the ordinary; it is *extra*-ordinary. This is real. Here nothing is missing. You want to come back here. You were never really away! No one ever is away from here – really.

' "You are always here. You and everyone else are parts of what *is*. I say *is* but that is to bring in the idea of time. But time, you see, is only a device – something that lets us talk about what *is*". '

15 Alive Again
at the Dead Sea

I once took a party of parishioners to Israel and we toured all
the usual Christian sites: The Church of the Annunciation in
Nazareth, the town of Bethlehem, Gethsemane, the Mount of
Olives and the Garden Tomb. One day we made a longer
excursion: down from Jerusalem to the Dead Sea.

And it really is *down*. Jerusalem is 2500 feet above sea level
and the Dead Sea is 1250 feet below – the lowest place on
earth. The road winds steeply therefore over the forty miles
or so from Jerusalem to Qumran where the Dead Sea Scrolls
were discovered in the 1940s.

For part of the way, this is also the Jericho Road,
mentioned in Jesus' parable, and there is still an 'Inn of the
Good Samaritan' in the bare rock of the Judean wilderness.
Only nowadays they sell Coca-Cola and pizzas. As you
descend, the climate changes. It is usually around eighty
degrees by the Dead Sea, but there is no humidity and so you
do not perspire uncomfortably. Also, because it is so
low-lying, harmful ultraviolet rays from the sun are filtered
through extra layers of atmosphere, allowing you to
sunbathe all day without burning. It is an ideal climate. No
wonder King Herod built palaces here!

At last we arrived by the shores of the great salt lake at
Qumran. There is a roadside cafe and a tourist shop and that
is all. Half a mile from the road are the caves, like black eyes
in the white cliff face. This is where, at the time of Jesus, the
Essenes lived. They were a strict religious sect: devout,
law-abiding and scholarly. Here they wrote their apocalyptic
texts about the coming Teacher of Righteousness and the

93

final battle between the forces of darkness and the angels of light.

It is the perfect setting for such a story. The country is dazzlingly bright by day as the high sun pours out of the cloudless sky, and perfectly dark at night – dark, so dark it is tangible like a soft cloth.

Among our party was Annie Butler, a cheerful woman of about 56 or 57. She had just taken early retirement from schoolteaching. Easy-going Annie, with a plump face that always wore a reassuring smile. But there was something the matter with her on this trip. She had been her usual self on the aeroplane – chattering on with anecdotes about children and religious education. Old jokes about pupils' drawings of the Holy Family on a Boeing 747: 'That's the flight into Egypt, Miss! And there's Pontius the pilot!' People laughed, though the tales had been told before.

One evening we were sitting out on the hotel balcony overlooking the Sea of Galilee – Capernaum and the traditional Mount of Transfiguration to our left and, away to the north, the looming outline of the much higher Mount Hermon.

'When did you say we were going down to the Dead Sea?'

'Thursday.'

'Do we have to?'

'Don't you want to go?'

'Not really, I like it here.'

That conversation by itself put me on my guard. It was so unlike Annie to talk like that. She was the game one among the whole crowd of them. It was she who would push on when the others were flagging. She who would want to see another historical site when everyone else was ready to call it a day. But, from the Monday night in Galilee onwards, she became more and more tense, nervous, diffident and, for her, unusually quiet.

On the Thursday morning she came to my room after breakfast as I was looking at the map and getting ready to meet the coach driver.

'Do I have to go, Peter?'

'You don't *have* to go, Annie. You don't have to do anything you don't want. But, come on, what's this all about? You've been a bag of nerves for the last three days, and it's not like you.'

She looked dressed for the Dead Sea, in her thin cotton dress and sandals. 'Are you feeling the heat?' I said, 'because it's going to be even hotter as we get down to Qumran.'

She looked startled. 'Oh, don't say it! I don't even like the sound of the place!'

'Now then, and what has Qumran – sorry, *that place* whose name we don't mention – done to you?'

'I don't know. Nothing. I just hate the whole idea. A sense of foreboding, if you like. Yes, call it foreboding.' .

'If you really feel so bad about it, stay here, and we'll pick you up on our way back this evening.'

But I knew she would come. Annie Butler is just not the giving-in sort. She gripped the strap on her shoulder bag as if she were screwing up her determination.

So steep and winding was the road – it was like sliding down the hypotenuse of a giddy triangle. We passed the blue monastery buildings which seemed barely balanced high up in the rocky gorge. Annie became distressed. She was trembling and trying not to let anyone know it. I was sitting beside her, but across the aisle. I leaned over: 'What's the matter? Would you like a drink?'

'It's all right. It's just that I know what we're coming to.'

Just then the bus lurched and skidded, and we slid to within a few feet of falling over into the ravine. I wondered if Annie had had some premonition of disaster. '… what we're coming to.' But it wasn't that.

We stopped outside the Qumran Tourist Centre in the blazing light. We were the only coach there as it was still quite early in the day. People got off the coach and sauntered over to the shop and cafe, while our driver – who was also our guide – called out for us all to reassemble by the Qumran postbox in fifteen minutes. Annie was trembling even more violently than before. I took her arm. She spoke through chattering teeth which she was trying to clench. 'I don't need him. I don't need the guide – any guide. I know very well what's here.'

She looked into the distance at the black caves and her eyes filled with tears. 'There,' she said, 'up there – that's where we lived. But the writing wasn't done there. Oh, no. The writing was done –' And she turned through 180 degrees and then

pointed to some little stone walls on the far side of the road –
'was done *there*!'

I said, 'I thought you hadn't been here before.'

'Come on and I'll show you.' We crossed the road and
walked between the little stone walls until we came to a place
which opened out a bit. 'Here we are,' she said. 'This is where
the writing got done.'

It had been reconstructed by the Israeli Museum
Authorities and sure enough there was a notice stuck in the
ground bearing the one word, 'Scriptorium'.

Having seen the place, Annie was calm again. 'You're
right, Peter. I haven't been here before *recently*. I was here
before though. And I could show you the path that leads
from here up to the cave in the cliff where I slept. I know it so
well, you see, because I used to walk it every day – except on
the Sabbath.

'I was a monk, one of the writers. I remember where I used
to stand ...' She thought for a minute and then pointed: 'Just
there. I can remember, too, copying out parts of the Book of
the Prophet Isaiah. That's when I first began to feel uneasy –
when we were in Jerusalem the other day and looking at
fragments of that Scroll in the museum. That was my job. I
worked on some of that.' She was good, old, smiley Annie
again.

She said, 'Come on, let's go and get an ice cream!'

16   Just Picture It

Perhaps we should not be too surprised when we hear of churchpeople getting mixed up in occult practices – after all, one sort of religion is akin to another. And there is a type of person who likes the taste of spiritual excitement, or at least the prospect of it: so he or she nibbles at New Age, crystals, dowsing, faith-healing, Guru so-and-so and Swami whatsisname, charismatic revival and the Toronto Blessing. It is a kind of consumerism of the spirit, a stroll through the supermarket of religions in the hope of picking up something on special offer.

It is not easy for a vicar to steer his more gullible parishioners away from the most dangerous excesses in these pseudo-religious and quasi-religious practices. People do not often tell him what they are up to, and usually the vicar gets to know about the trouble only when it is too late. This is especially true in parishes where there are house groups: so much psychosexual energy is generated in such groups that the results can be unpredictable – harmfully so.

From the time of Elymas the Magician and Simon Magus, some people have always coveted spiritual power and secret knowledge, the hidden ability to shape events and the desire for psychic authority and wealth. Others use religion as psychotherapy or for an ego trip. Unfortunately, house groups have more than their share of these sorts of dabblers.

The members of one of our prayer groups were disturbed by the activities of a newcomer – Anne Rawson, from Huddersfield, a divorcee in her twenties who had been instructing them in the practice of visualization, telling them that it was, 'like prayer only in hyper-drive'. According to Anne, all you had to do was achieve a meditative state and hold before your mind for twenty minutes or so the object which you wished to possess or the event that you hoped would come to pass. You would, if you were doing it right, get your heart's desire. The group had mentioned all this to me because Anne was forever holding forth on the art of visualization and so monopolizing the house meetings. Also, they sensed there was something unhealthy about the whole business, but they did not want to upset Anne who, they knew, had had a tough time since the breakdown of her marriage and was only just, with the help of the group, beginning to get back on her feet.

I decided to visit Anne at her home. She was a vivacious woman: very much the red sweater and short skirt type, alert, quick-eyed and no amateur in the art of sexual nuance. She was busy in her clean, bright kitchen when I called.

'So they've sent you to warn me off, have they?' She was nothing if not direct. I tried to disarm her by saying that I simply wanted to know a bit more about what had been going on at the house group.

'Not a lot, Vicar, if you ask me. They're a pretty wooden lot, aren't they – begging your pardon! I've tried to tell them – you can get beyond prayer you know – to a higher consciousness. I know, because I've done it.'

She folded her arms robustly and stood with the triumphant stance of one who had just finished a heavy round of spring cleaning. 'I visualized a holiday in Florida – and I got it' – the words almost stuck between her teeth. 'And I'll tell you another thing: this house, the garden, the whole lot – all just as I pictured it. You can have anything you want, if you want it enough. Did you know that, Vicar?'

'Yes, I know it.'

My reply seemed to startle her, but she soon recovered her confidence. 'People – your people –' she said, 'pray, but they're groundlings and they don't understand the full power of prayer. As I see it, prayer is an evolutionary thing, it develops as we progress.'

'And you're saying that the people at St Mark's are still monkeys, are you?'

'Sort of. They think it's just a matter of asking for things and hoping that God will give you what you want.'

'No, they don't. They know that prayer is much more like

a sustained effort on our part to see what God wants.'

'That's moralizing baloney – to get people to behave quietly, force them into line.'

'But what if God knows best?'

'Leave God out of it. That's just part of a primitive way of looking at things. There's no Old Man in the sky. And prayer isn't a matter of talking to anyone. It's a case of learning to influence physical events by the power of thought.'

She put coffee cups and a plate of biscuits on a silver tray and led me into the sitting-room. It was elegantly, even opulently, furnished, though there was something of a clash between the green of the sofa and the vehement red of Anne's skirt. She gave me the whole lecture about the need to raise one's consciousness and to seek a higher way of being. All this could be achieved by training in visualization.

I said, 'You're making out that it's something quite exalted spiritually. But does a higher grade of mind really want to use the technique of visualization to procure holidays in Florida and a show house?'

That caught her on the raw. She lit a cigarette. 'That's only the beginning. You progress from what's simple to higher things. Anyhow, there's nothing wrong with material pleasures – that's one of the faults of the Church: it's so downbeat when it comes to enjoyment.'

The room was warm and scented. Wisps of cigarette smoke played around the vases of flowers, and exotic fishes moved meaningfully in a huge aquarium opposite the window.

I asked Anne about her life before she had come to live in Leeds. 'Oh, that – it was all wrong, that was. I can see it all now. 'Course, I couldn't at the time. That was my downfall. But it's all over with. My ex-husband – well, he was a brute, if you want to know. No finesse. There was no way I was going to spend the rest of my life with Ken.

'It's all past and gone and I'm clear of it. I won't be on my own for ever, you'll see. I'm working on it. I've just the guy in mind.'

'You're visualizing him too, are you?'

'Why not?'

'Because – have you ever thought – you might get what you desire.'

'That's the whole idea.'

'But gifts often come with barbs. They have consequences. You've read Grimm's fairy tales ...'

'Fairytales!'

She began to tell me that she was in the process of visualizing a real go-getter: a six-foot, suave entrepreneur 'with some charisma – most unKenlike, in fact.'

She got him too, or someone like him – except I'm not sure that he was quite six foot. They were married, and they moved into a large Georgian house on the Otley Road. She wasn't in church often after that, but they both came to Midnight Communion at Christmas and bubbled with tales about their travels to New York, Delhi and Buenos Aires, 'on business.'

They had two children in next to no time. I'm not certain about what sort of future Anne visualized for them – but, in any case, it would be one without a father. While they were small, her paragon left her and set up house with another woman, a business associate. Anne took to drink and her GP phoned one day to let me know that she had swallowed some pills. She would be in Leeds Infirmary for a while. Her mother – helped by some of the St Mark's folk – were looking after the children.

I went to see Anne. She was remarkably self-possessed and ironical for one who had recently been so ill. 'Thanks for coming, Vicar. I'll get over this – it's only a fairytale, isn't it?'

17   The Spirit
of the Masai Mara

Carol Marsden was Sacristan at my church in Tockwith, near York. In 1988 she won a competition in a national newspaper for what she described as 'a very upmarket safari' in Kenya. Carol was the right sort of person for the Sacristan's job: meticulous, punctual and dedicated. The sacred vessels were put out for the Holy Communion with great care and precision. Different colours for vestments were required to suit different feast and fast days. Carol could be relied upon never to get the colours wrong, or the time of service wrong, or indeed anything wrong that was in any way connected with the organization of the Sanctuary.

It was not her job to clean the Sanctuary, but she cleaned and polished it anyway. The chalice and paten always gleamed and yet – bane of the parson's liturgical life, this can be – they never tasted or smelt of silver polish! I would miss her for the three Sundays that she was to be away. Her preparations for her absence were elaborate: she left little notes and reminders everywhere, 'And,' she said, 'there's enough wine in the cask and enough wafers in the vestry cupboard to last you a month.'

Her personal preparations were equally thorough, including two cameras to photograph the wild life, 'And a new pair of lightweight binoculars. We have to travel light because,' she said, trying to sound blasé, 'we're to be in small aircraft for most of the journeys: Mombasa, Nairobi, Ol Donyo Wuas, Funzi Island ...' She was enjoying this recital of exotica. She was unmarried.

A fortnight after her return, she showed colour slides in the parish hall and supplied a beautifully composed commentary. 'The animals moved in their own space. Even the large ones moved with an almost silent elegance. Such power held in restraint. Then, when they did cry out, the sound of them was of Africa itself.

'Most impressive of all were the Masai tribespeople. Limbs black as ebony, they can run like cheetahs. Here's a picture of eleven boys on a lion hunt. It's a puberty rite with them. They run the lion to death and then they spear him. Two or three Masai are eaten by lions every year in the village. They accept this. It is the way of things.'

On the following Sunday I arrived for the eight o'clock service to discover that the Sanctuary had not been made ready. It was unheard of. I rushed round and just about managed to get the service started on time. Carol came in in the middle of it and sat in the congregation. After it was over, she came to apologize tearfully extravagantly.

'It doesn't matter, Carol. Don't upset yourself so. Anyone's allowed to be late now and again. I've slept in myself before today.'

She was frantic. 'I didn't sleep in, Peter. I had a devil of a night. In fact every night this week has been a devil of a night. Can I come and talk to you, please?'

It was the Carol Service that evening, so there was no other morning service after the eight o'clock. 'Come across now and we'll have a cup of coffee. I don't have to dash off anywhere.'

This woman of normally serene disposition was fidgeting at my elbow like an over-excited schoolgirl. She could hardly walk straight, and she kept knocking into things as we made our way out through the west door and locked up behind us. But it was her eyes that were the most disturbing. She stared so. And she kept looking about her. There was only one word for it: haunted.

In the vicarage she said, 'Do I smell?' It was the sort of question to bring you up with a bit of a start. 'No,' she said, 'I don't mean B.O. or anything like that. I mean do I smell peculiar? Do I smell of Africa?'

'I'm not sure I'd know for certain what Africa smells like.'

She sank into the armchair and she looked calmer. She was an attractive woman – neat, fortyish, slim, the sort who wears good quality skirts and smart shoes. Today she was wearing a pleated yellow skirt and an ivory blouse.

'I'd better tell you the whole story – as much as I know. I was absolutely knocked out by Africa, by the Masai particularly. They are so noble, so cultivated, though they live in the wilds. Six thousand feet up there in the middle of nowhere on the Masai Mara – the place is as full of signs and meanings to them as the map of the London Underground is to you and me.

'Cultured, that's what they are. We had a Masai guide for three days' safaris. He made fire by rubbing sticks. He could see things when we saw nothing: animals, aeroplanes ... anything. He knew what the weather was going to do.

'He was so tall and slender – they all were – and his arms and legs were like polished jet. A lovely big, wide, carefree smile.'

'What was his name?'

'Mugumo.' There was a silence. Then she said, 'I know what you're thinking – you're thinking I got a thing about him, aren't you? Well, it wasn't just Mugumo: they were all wonderful.

'You know they live on cows' blood. They bleed the cow and drink the blood with the milk. Then they stop up the wound and return the cow to the herd. That's what I call a really reusable resource.

'They took me into one of their dwellings: clay and straw-built huts. There's a fire in the middle. It gets cold up on the Mara at night.'

I could tell by the way she said 'Mara' that she had almost gone native there.

'You know, the husband and wife don't sleep with each other until they want a child. The old folk sometimes ask to be left out in the country to be taken by the animals when they sense they're nearing the end of their lives. It's a whole *culture*, I tell you. A whole way of being.

'The girls are circumcised too. It sounds gruesome, but somehow when you're there it seems the right thing.'

After saying this, Carol broke down into furious sobs. 'The trouble is,' she said, 'it's all come back with me. My bedroom smells of Mara. It's full of the sounds of the plateau, all night, night after night. I've washed and cleaned all my things. I'm not one to have grubby things about me.'

No one who knew Carol would have imagined she would have for a moment. Still, 'perhaps on a pair of walking shoes?'

'I've scrubbed them. Besides they're in the shed. They've never been anywhere near the bedroom. And it's not just the smells. It's the sounds, I tell you. Africa. The animals. Even the light – the light in the garden is like that on the plain.

'Last night – this is why I'm in such a state, why I was late – something was actually in the room with me. In the bed. It was … well, if it had been English, I would have said "medieval". And the smell of that hot mixture – milk and blood.'

Carol Marsden was not an unsophisticated woman. I guess she knew her Freud as well as she knew the old English literature which she taught at the grammar school.

'Has talking about it done any good?'

'Yes, of course it has. Well, you can see it has. I've calmed down now. But I must explain. The reason I was late this morning wasn't because I slept in. I simply *had* to get that smell out of my nostrils. I cleaned the bedroom, stripped the bed and put new sheets on. I went over the place like spring cleaning. Still I'm nervous about going back home.

'Will you come and say a prayer, a blessing in the house? I don't mean an exorcism, or anything extreme like that. Just a house-blessing, a rehallowing.'

'Now, if you like. I'm on my way to Wetherby, and I'm seeing someone there at eleven o'clock. I can drop you off if you like.'

In the car she was more like her old self again. Calm. Quiet. Her hands clasped over the pleated skirt. Almost serene. This was the Carol I had known for nine years.

She said she would make the coffee this time while I went to say a prayer in the upstairs rooms. When I came down, she was sitting in front of the fire. 'All right?'

'All right,' I said. 'But you did say you'd cleaned and tidied the place this morning, put new sheets on the bed?'

'Yes, that's why I was late – I explained.'

I had to tell her what I had found: 'The place looks as if a bomb's hit it. Sheets and pillows all over the floor. And there's a smell … something organic, as you said, like milk and blood or something. Warm. Pungent.'

I made her look at it. 'I wasn't lying Peter. I simply don't understand it. I did clean up – I know I did. Well, I'll just have to do it all again.'

She was in church as usual the next week, and the next and the next after that. Then, on the Thursday following, she came to see me. 'I'm sorry but I'm going to have to give up being Sacristan. I don't even know why – quite. All I can say is that I've changed, somehow. Or something seems to have changed me. And I'm going away – leaving.

'I'm going to live with my sister in Bath. It's all arranged. I've given in my notice and the house is up for sale. I don't know what I'll do. I might go back to teaching, and then I might not. But I do know that I've just got to move from here. I feel as if I'm *being* moved.'

Six months after that there was a letter from Carol's sister in Bath to say that Carol had died of a tumour on the brain. She had left a few hundred pounds to the Church in her will.

18   Captain Hoare

Alan Steward was in the mental hospital – the old manor house now invisible from the road because of the new buildings in concrete and glass. It always seemed to be sunny there and the grounds had been planted with willows and precise flower beds. It was as if the outside had been designed to provide relief from the turmoil within.

Alan was in the day room which was dazzlingly lit by the low sun and smelt of cleanliness. The staff were almost incognito and the patients were calm. Alan was getting better, nearly ready to come home. It would be a lonely homecoming because his wife had left him, taking their eight-year-old daughter, Amy, with her. He had tried to kill them both with a carving knife, but, by some fluke or mother's instinct, Jan had seized the copper frying pan and brained him with it. 'I kept thinking he was dead,' she told me over and over again after the ambulance had taken him away and the police had gone.

He had been concussed – nothing worse – and after a couple of days in the General Hospital, they removed him to The Willows. He had told the police: 'The Captain made me do it.' Later he told me the whole story.

My mates in the print works brought in a ouija board and we used to play it in the tea break and at lunchtime – for a laugh. It was a laugh alright and, sort of mystifying. It would spell out all our names. Then one day we asked it for its own name and it spelt 'Captain Hoare'.

Well, the lads seemed to get tired of it. You know how it is. You get bored. I wasn't bored though and I asked if I could take it home. Jan wouldn't touch it with a barge pole – she's Catholic you see – so I got to playing it by myself when she'd

gone to bed. I asked it once to tell me my wife's name and it
spelt out 'Jeanette', just like that. God knows how it knew. I
mean, no one ever called her Jeanette. It was always just Jan.
It spelt Amy as well. Amy Marie.

Then I got the idea of asking it to tell me something really
useful. And it did. I'll say it did! It gave me race winners. I'll
always remember the first: 'King's Breakfast' at Sandown –
twelve to one. I won £120.

Trouble was, it didn't always give winners. Sometimes
when I put my finger on the glass and whispered my question,
it would move to a strange jumble of letters and I couldn't
make out any clear message. Other times it just wouldn't
move at all. Then after a few days like this it would return to
form and give a couple of good 'uns: ten to one – thirty-three
to one once.

I got to asking it – joking like – 'Are you on form today,
Captain, or what?'

It was high summer when Alan first told me his tale. We
were sitting at the white table on the edge of the lawn. So
warm it was and benign. But his story turned my stomach. I
have often noticed this reaction to evil in myself and in others
– not so much an outright dread as a nauseous sensation –
the sort of feeling that overcomes you near a blocked sewer.

He was still under mild sedation – a gentle weaning from
the strong sedation he had been under for a fortnight. We had
come out into the mellow air and the birdsong to pray. Alan
knew that he needed deliverance. First he must tell the rest of
his story.

'I got really friendly with the Captain. Jan was mad as hell.
She said it was worse than me taking another woman. I'll
admit it, I did get to staying up late. It was unhealthy, she
said. "Unwholesome" – that was Jan's word for it.

'We had rows. I said, "It's not unwholesome when I can
give you an extra fifty quid for the housekeeping, is it!" '

Across the lawn, people strolled in sun hats and short
sleeves. They were putting up the red-and-white marquee for
the Open Day. The sun reflected violently in the ranks of
windows. It could not have been brighter. But I felt an intense
darkness. Alan was like a man home from the battlefield and
sick with what he had seen there.

'It got so bad that Jan threatened to leave me. I told

Captain Hoare about this. I used to chat to him, you see, as I arranged the alphabet on the table. I put the glass in the middle and all the letters cut out and in a ring. I'd get myself a glass of whisky and settle down for a good long session, chattering away about this and that.

'When I mentioned Jan was threatening to leave me ...' I remember precisely that phrase of Alan's. It was so *normal*, banal even. As if he had been talking to me or his mates instead of to a polished upturned bowl. There was nothing spooky about it. The occult had become a way of life with him.

When I said she was going to leave me, he moved fast. He gave me three horses and I put them in a tenner treble and three crossed doubles. I won eighteen hundred quid. I waited until Amy came home from Sunday School then, when we'd finished lunch, I put the lot on the table in fifty pound notes. 'Is that healthy enough for you?' I said.

She was a lot less angry about Captain Hoare after that, I can tell you.

Then the nasty business started. I woke up one night, and Jan was screaming at me wild-eyed. It seems I'd been trying to do something to her, sexually. Not the usual thing. Something bad. Well, I'd dreamt about it. I woke up and I was actually doing it – or I'd been having a damn good try. Jan was crying, trembling – bared her teeth at me. I could see she was terrified. I was shocked, yes, but I have to admit I was bloody excited, het up. I'd never known such a strong feeling. Lust. But it wasn't right.

Over by the main buildings they were rehearsing the tannoy. The day had become even warmer and a few clouds boiled up and sent their shadows racing across the grass.

I calmed her down and said I was sorry. She was still shaking and she put her dressing gown on. 'You just keep away from me, that's all!' she said. We never had – you know, proper relations, after that.

Next morning I got up and went downstairs as usual. All the family photographs had been turned face down and there was a nasty smell about the place. That was the day we learned that the print works was moving to Swansea and there was no job for me.

Jan went all to pieces when I told her. 'It's your fault!' she shouted. 'It's all your fault – it's because of your meddling!'

I was in a mess right enough. I suppose I thought that the only person who could help was Captain Hoare. Jan was right, though: I was spending more time with him than with her and the kid.

That night I got the glass out as usual and, while I was arranging the letters, I prattled on to the Captain. When I sat down, I saw something, someone in the rocking chair in the corner. It was a man in a naval uniform. He was just staring at me, smiling. Then he looked at me like a cat looks at its dinner.

I said, 'Who are you?'

He laughed and his yellow face seemed to crack. He said, 'Don't tell me you don't recognize *me*, Alan! I'm the Captain of your soul!'

The rest of the night – I don't know how long – he talked on and on and absolutely convinced me that I had to kill Jan and Amy. For their own good. 'Really, my friend, it's nothing. And you'll see it's for the best. Then I can really show you how to start to live.'

'Start to live ... Start to live ...' – the words were in my head, ringing like your ears do after an anaesthetic. You know the rest. That Friday I got the kitchen knife ... God knows what would have happened if she hadn't hit me.

What was to be done? We had made a beginning. I took the glass to the hospital and, in front of Alan, said aloud the ancient one-line prayer of exorcism over it: 'Depart, unclean spirit, in the name of the Father, the Son and the Holy Ghost.' Then we smashed it and put it in the hospital incinerator.

Alan made his confession and I said prayers for his deliverance. Now he has returned home, but Jan will not go back to him. He is chastened, truly sorry, and he comes to church most weeks. He managed to find a new job with the Water Board. I joked with him that it ought to have been the Holy Water Board – that would keep him out of trouble!

What was it all about – a mid-life crisis made worse by a run of bad luck and redundancy? A sudden bout of schizophrenia? Whatever the explanation, the case had been dripping with evil. I know; I could smell it.

19   King Alfred's Castle

In Meanwood, Leeds, there is an old ruin known locally as King Alfred's Castle. Youngsters scramble there, and families take their picnics. In days gone by it used to be an even more picturesque relic: that was when it was surrounded by woods, but now the woods have been cleared and the ghost of King Alfred, if ever he walks forth, must do so along the edge of a small housing development.

The ruin is said to be haunted. Many have testified to seeing blue lights over the place in the darkness, and someone even published what he claimed was a photograph of a ghost captured there in 1949. It looks eerie when it is silhouetted against the western sky.

I used to visit an old lady, Alice Townsend, who lived in one of the 1930s houses in Church Lane, just across the road from King Alfred's Castle. Alice was rather eerie herself. The youngsters called her 'the witch' and, to be truthful, she looked the part. She had been married, but George died in the 1950s, and she now lived with her son Eric.

They managed somehow to be strangely compatible. Alice was a Rosicrucian, a member of an old Order which was connected with the Knights Templar and which claimed for itself the sometime allegiance of many celebrated thinkers. The great philosopher Rene Descartes (1596-1650) was said to have been a member. In England in the 1980s Rosicrucianism was a minority interest, to put it no lower. There are perhaps only a few thousand adherents in the land.

As a devotee, Alice was a keen admirer, and even a practitioner, of ancient wisdom in its practical application; and she professed esoteric knowledge. I am not expert enough to vouch for the purity of Alice's Rosicrucianism: it seemed to be all of a piece with Tarot, horoscopes and amateur clairvoyance in her repertoire and conversation.

Eric had other interests which in some ways could not have been further from those of his mother, but which in other ways left you in no doubt that he was his mother's son. Whereas Alice was locked in the past and the ancient treasury of wisdom, both homespun and exotic, Eric always had his eyes on the future. He talked endlessly about the millennium – and this was only 1988! He was a UFO freak. He owned a personal computer, and he took all the science magazines. For his daily work, he was a laboratory technician at Leeds University. He was also the narrator of the most intriguing ghost story I have ever heard.

One night, on his way home from a party in Moortown, he had seen blue lights over King Alfred's Castle. He was on foot, so he stopped to investigate. I could just imagine him: Eric the intrepid, Eric the unabashed – he was not one to be put off by ghostly tales – traipsing over the wet fields in the moonlight on his way to check out the old ruin for vibrations. He looked for scientific explanations as a schoolboy looks for conkers.

He said he saw ghostly figures – 'they were surrounded by a sort of electric blue light that moved with them' – and these did not disperse even when he drew near.

Alice said, 'There was a monastery on or near the site, long ago. They would be monks.'

'They didn't look like monks, Mother.'

Alice could embroider a story in the time it takes to brew a cup of tea. And she could tell it with such nonchalance, with such an air of understated authority, that, what is more, you tended to believe her. She was sure that the ghostly vision was of monks who had been dispossessed, and possibly even killed, at the time of the dissolution of the monasteries. 'There were Rosicrucians among the monks, you know,' she said with proprietorial zeal, 'and among the clergy.'

'Nonsense, Mother! They weren't monks at all.'

But she had spoken with such certainty that you felt compelled to believe her interpretation.

'I know who they were. And I've told you before: I communed with them.'

Why, I wondered, would a lab technician, aged

thirty-eight, choose a table-rapper's word like 'communed'? He uttered the word with such an absence of guile or of striving for effect that I felt more inclined to believe what he had to say: that is, I am convinced he had been deluded but I was sure he wasn't lying.

'They moved in and out of the old stone buildings as if the structures weren't there at all. At first they didn't look at me or speak to me; but I knew *they* knew I was around. Their walking was so deliberate that I felt they were fulfilling an important task. It looked like a ritual – Mother says it would have been a religious ritual – but it seemed somehow more urgent than that.

'There was no sound. They weren't speaking but I could tell they were communicating with one another. It was a very intense atmosphere. They were quite oblivious of the stone walls.'

'Now, that's a ghost for you,' Alice interrupted with what she obviously thought was a clincher. 'Ghosts walk through walls.'

'One of them,' said Eric in a matter-of-fact tone, 'walked right through me. I didn't feel it. I didn't feel anything except that the figures were really preoccupied, as if they were anxious about something.'

Even an old occult practitioner like Alice was rather fazed by this remark.

'Altogether,' said Eric, 'I saw them on three separate occasions. I was mad keen to know who or what they were. They might have been simply energy, light, on another waveband. I never spoke all the time I was up there with them. There was no need to. I was sure they could tell what I was thinking anyhow.

I was aware of having thoughts, having questions, and somehow projecting these to the strange figures. After talking to Mother about them, I wanted to know whether they were from the time of the dissolution of the monasteries or from another historical period.

They just kept on coming and going, as before. But I feel sure they had picked up my wonderings, as a question. It was strange. The one nearest to me seemed to smile. Then another stood right in front of me and said ...

Well, he didn't *say*. He just sort of plonked the sentence in

my mind. I mean, I didn't *hear* it – not with my ears anyway.
He said – what I heard was 'We're not from the past, Eric ...'
– my name, I thought; how does he ... it, know my name? ...
'we're from the future.'

Then he said, 'What *you* call the future. Time, you see is
only a construct. It has no reality except as a mystical context
for morality.'

'You see,' said Alice. 'There you go. That's monks' talk, if
ever I heard it!'

'You're sure you heard rightly?' I asked.

'Oh, yes,' he said. 'And I wrote it down as soon as I got
home.'

I wondered for a moment, and I have wondered again
since, whether Eric made up the whole tale as a part of his
rivalry with his mother. As if he had been looking for a way
to say, 'Why should all wisdom come from the past? Look,
I've received some from the future!'

But on reflection I am inclined to believe him precisely
because he was so unemphatic about the whole thing. He
reported it as one might report on the state of the traffic in
town. And that saying about time and morality: it is so
elegant, so thought-provoking. I don't think it was something
which his mother had read to him out of Descartes.

20 Cursed Bees

Jane Girling lay in a side ward in Bolton Royal Infirmary recovering from more than a hundred bee stings. Jane was one of the stalwart ladies of the parish, a fresh-faced fifty year old married to a market gardener and with more energy than the national grid. She was also Secretary of the Parochial Church Council – a task which she performed with the sort of unobtrusive efficiency that is every vicar's dream.

She would take on any task, and, when Harriet Martindale fell ill, it was Jane who volunteered to supervise the organization of the annual church garden party. This was always held at the old colonel's house, The Beeches, on the Horwich Road, under the shelter of Rivington Pike: here the lawns were wide and the gardens well-kept, so it was, by a long way, the best venue for the garden party in the whole parish.

In the old days, church garden parties were mainly intended as social occasions, and an opportunity for sempiternal rural England to parade itself; for the parish to observe itself as a great institution at play, and to gather strength and encouragement from the spectacle. Really, the old-style garden party was a secular, social ritual. Above all it was meant to be very definitely leisure.

But in recent times it has become a fundraising opportunity and the one big event in the year by which the parish church hopes to bring in sufficient cash to pay the bills for the next twelve months. It had to be, as the Colonel had said in his more active days, 'organized with military precision.'

'To do is fine, but to delegate is sublime' was Jane's motto and she was quite brilliant at all the necessary administration. She worked by appointing little teams of volunteers – though

it is doubtful whether anyone who ever worked for Jane
Girling would describe himself as a volunteer – whose
responsibility would be for individual aspects of the
goings-on. So there was a refreshments team, a white
elephant team, a produce team and so on through the whole
repertoire.

Norma Malcolm was put – I mean volunteered – in charge
of the entertainments team. Norma was usually described as
'fussy'. She spoke loudly and dressed in a rather
unco-ordinated style – smart blouse above a pair of
knee-length shorts, that sort of thing. I once heard one of the
choirmen refer to her as 'a bit of a comic turn'. Norma had
ideas. 'I've got ideas for this entertainment,' she had told Jane
and the rest of us at the first meeting of the Standing
Committee. Well, that was all right with Jane. Her admirable
method was to deploy her troops and leave it to them to get
on with the fighting.

Late June and the day was almost upon us. It was left to us
only to pray for fair weather. And so it turned out. An
English summer day in which time seemed to stand still in the
heat. The garden colours perfect in the sunlight. Crowds
came – and not just locals, but motorists with their families
out for the day from Manchester. The only mild complaint
was from the ladies on the cake stall, who said that the
chocolate was melting.

Everyone was in mellow mood except Norma. She was on
edge, nervously looking this way and that, frequently leaving
the hoop-la stall to trot down to the front gate and peer out
as if she was expecting someone. As it turned out she was
expecting someone.

At about half-past four, a woman and a girl came up the
drive and began to set up something at the corner of the lawn
– something that looked a bit like a deck chair and a bit like
an army field latrine. 'That's old Rose and her scruffy
daughter!' called out Mrs May on the produce stall.

Norma ran to help them put up what was in fact a small
tent. That was when there occurred the explosion – not
dynamite, but Jane Girling: 'Norma!' she shouted so loudly
that the whole crowd stopped in mid-enjoyment, 'What the
hell d'you think you're doing?'

Norma was setting up a small table and chair in front of

the tent. Jane ran to where the newly arrived women and Norma were putting up their stall. I followed at a distance and managed to catch up with Jane before she had reached them. 'Jane, Jane! Let's try to avoid a nasty scene.'

'It's all right you saying that, Vicar, but I was at the cricket club gala last year when Rose came telling fortunes and the like, and she thoroughly frightened more than a few. It's not that I think there's actually anything in what she prophesies – it's a load of old rubbish if you ask me. But she's nasty with it. She drinks and she likes winding people up, upsetting them. She frightens people, I tell you.'

The crowd were obviously regarding all this as the best entertainment of the day.

'Norma!' Jane bellowed, 'I told you you weren't to ask Rose to come today.'

Norma, ungainly and not knowing which way to look, still stood her ground: 'It's only a bit of fun.'

'And I say it isn't only a bit of fun!' Then she went over to the gypsy woman and her daughter: 'Off with you! Come on –'

'What's it got to do with you? This lady invited us.' Old Rose spoke as if she had a knife between her teeth.

'And *this* lady is telling you to go! Now – off with you, both of you!'

The girl said, 'My mam's not doing nobody no harm' and pulled a sour face.

But Jane was vehement: 'I saw your mischief at the cricket gala and I'm not having my garden party spoilt by your spite. Now ... ouch!'

She stopped in her tracks. It was a bee sting. Rose's face was all sardonic delight: 'That'll teach you, *lady*! And there's more where that came from. I know the bees and the bees know me. You'd better look out!'

Jane had recovered her composure by now and there was no stopping her. She almost bundled the woman out. Norma just stood there, hopping from one leg to the other. The incident entered local folklore for this reason: nine days later, Jane was walking in the Chinese Gardens, created by Lord Leverhulme, when she was attacked by a swarm of bees, only moderately injured but very severely frightened.

Even after her discharge from hospital, she never seemed to

regain her famous organizing ability. 'I've lost all my confidence,' she said.

21 The Hill

Youth club kids on church-sponsored hikes sing dubious songs as they bowl along. I was on one such hike, up Ingleborough Hill in the Yorkshire Dales – sponsorship money to go towards sheet music for the choir's centenary appeal. When the youngsters got as far as, 'There was a young man from St Paul's … who …', I dropped back and walked beside the youth leader, Alan Rhodes, who, being past sixty, was an old hand at these rural rambles.

Alan was the outdoor type. I supposed he had been born in a pair of walking boots and that if you were to chop his leg into sections, you would see it said 'Youth work' all the way through – like Blackpool rock. It had been his vocation: first as Scoutmaster, then as an Area Commissioner in that movement and latterly as a paid youth worker with the local authority.

It was late April. All pastel shades and daffodils. The grass blew in silent ripples as if an invisible comb were being drawn through it. 'Look at that, will you?' Alan, pipe clenched in his teeth, was exultant. 'Ingleborough – that old anvil of a hill is as good as Table Mountain and just right for the Dales. It's all a matter of scale. 2373 feet. Anything bigger would look out of place here.'

It was a magnificent sight in the distance. Slightly forbidding, I thought, and I recalled Wordsworth's fear, which he set down in *The Prelude*, about the sight of a black mountain after nightfall in the Lake District. The age and the size of the hill is what impresses the feelings and produces an unsettled sensation in the pit of the stomach, especially if you are out alone towards dark.

I was talking about this with Alan: 'Wordsworth imagined

the crag was pursuing him,' I said.

'It's easy to imagine that,' said Alan. 'The hills do seem to move – especially on a darkening skyline. But I know something worse than that.' And he told me about a day and a night he had spent on Ingleborough twenty years earlier.

It started off as a day like this, but earlier – March, I think. Yes, March. I'd had a hell of a winter. Flu. Bad back. One thing after another. Anyhow, I looked out at the weather this particular day, and I thought to hell with it – I'm not staying in the house any longer.

I put my walking boots in the car and drove up to Clapham village. I reckoned a good walk up the old hill would do me a power of good – better than any doctor's pills.

I had to go steady. You know how it is when you've had a bad chest cold and you haven't stirred yourself for a week or two. I was a bit short of breath. If you come up from Clapham, it's not such a steep climb, but it's a long haul. There's a plateau. You're exposed for a long time and you seem to be getting nowhere. Actually, you're gaining height, slowly.

There's no warning. Suddenly the top comes into view. That's the Wordsworth frisson. It's startling. It looms – makes you dizzy. It's ancient and it's grand. And you're so small and in a little while you'll be gone. It's really scary, that. Weird. I'd say it's religious, Peter. Puts you in your place.

Well, I felt OK so I decided to walk on the last three-quarters of a mile to the summit. That was when the mist came down, as it can do at that time of the year. It played havoc with my breathing. So damp. And I've always been a touch asthmatic ...

The youngsters had got quite a way ahead of us and I called out for them to slow down a bit. Alan was in the grip of his own story by this time and I could tell from his eyes that he was reliving it.

I realized after a while that I was wandering around pretty aimlessly. I couldn't see the summit any more – couldn't see anything. Then I did see something. At first it was just like something in the corner of my eye, as if I'd got a hair caught. Then I realized it wasn't.

It was a figure, all in black, just on the edge of the mist. I called out, but there was no answer. Oh God, the feeling comes back to me even now! It never got any nearer or further away. It moved with me. I walked briskly. I ran, stumbled and stopped time and again. I was out of breath by now, I can tell you. And it wasn't all due to exertion. I was terrified.

I called out to it, but of course there was no answer. It wasn't an illusion. It wasn't something I was seeing *through* the mist. It was a human – well, let's put it like this, it was man-shaped.

Then, a strange thing. It was as if I heard words in my head: 'This way!' it seemed to say, 'This way!' I was really tired now and very short of breath. I thought I would faint. I must have been desperate. I thought, 'Why not?' And I started to walk towards the black figure. In any case, I was well and truly lost.

It never drifted any further away and, thank heaven, it didn't get any nearer either. I stumbled on. By this time I was on the point of collapse. Suddenly, the mist lifted and I was in the clear. The sun lit the place with a pale yellow light. And the black figure had gone. There, below me, was Clapham village. I could feel the warmth of the sun on my back. I nearly wept with relief.

We caught up with the kids and scrambled with them to the summit where we sat to eat our sandwiches. It was a heavenly day. It could not have been less threatening, less ghostly. This was good old England and its lovely, friendly countryside.

As we tucked into our eggs and cress, Amanda Halton came across and said, 'Do you believe in ghosts, Vicar? Do you, Alan?' 'What,' I said, 'on a day like this! What makes you ask?'

'Because,' she said, 'you know that side of the mountain – over there, the track that comes up from Clapham? It's haunted. By a friendly ghost though. A dead shepherd and they call him Black Tom. They say he comes and leads people to safety when there's a mountain mist –'

22 Cheerfulness Breaks In

Dennis Kelly was dragging himself around like a man upon whom the sorrows of the ages had fallen. He drifted past me and out of the church door after Evensong with not so much as a word. That was not in character, he was of the 'Old School', a man who was unfailingly polite. I called him back.

'Tummy bug – after effects,' was his explanation. But he looked steadily at me as he spoke, and his eyes were full of noble concealment. The rain was lashing into the porch. It suited Dennis' mood. 'I haven't been right since Father died.'

That was the clue. I said, 'Were you very close, you and your father?'

'Not as much as ...' But he turned away in mid-sentence and set off into the dark.

I ran after him and put a hand on his shoulder. 'Come across and have a whisky. It'll warm your stomach.' He came with me but unenthusiastically, like a prisoner giving himself up.

I resurrected the log fire and drew the curtains. 'It's kind of you, Peter. But really I'm just a big baby. Father, you see: that's what this is all about. I'm sorry I broke down back there, but it was when you asked me if we were close.

Truth is, he infuriated me with his self-absorption and what I took to be his hypochondria. To hear him talk, he was always at death's door. For years he said he had a dicky heart. We all knew it was no more than indigestion. Then the headaches. But worst of all, the depression – an ongoing down-in-the-dumpsness that he used to project, made you feel as if it was your fault. When you went to see him and he was in one of these, it was like walking into a funeral parlour.

Not that I did go to see him much. It took courage, I tell

you; and there was absolutely no incentive to call on him. I stayed away. Then he would phone in that maudlin, sentimental style: 'Your old man won't be around for much longer, Dennis.'

Or he would write his melancholy notes with embarrassing, bleeding heart verses in them. I was convinced – I said to my wife, many a time – it was all a scheme to make us guilty and beholden. The kids hated to visit their grandad because he would ask outright, 'Do you love your grandpa?' It made me squirm.

Then he got cancer. Leukaemia. And it saw him off in six weeks.

Dennis sat slumped, his head in his hands. Like father, like son, I thought. If he could have seen himself! He pulled himself together and apologized again. I said, 'There's no need to keep on saying sorry. These are human feelings.'

'I'm sorry,' he said, apologizing for apologizing. 'It's just that I wish I'd made more of him, seen him more often. I wish I'd seized my courage and charged down his gloominess, taken him out of himself. But I hadn't the stomach for it and it all seemed like a waste of time, a waste of my life. I was selfish, you see.'

We talked for an hour or more and downed a few more glasses of Scotch. I decided on the full-frontal attack: 'Look,' I said, 'free floating guilt is one of the most negative and destructive emotions anyone can feel. You know that old prayer, "Heavenly Father, give us grace to change the things we can change and to accept the things we cannot change, and the wisdom to tell the difference between them ...'

'Shut yourself in your bedroom or, better still, go out into a field and say out loud, "I'm sorry, Father – I should have been more understanding." Then get on with the rest of your life.'

Was that a brutal thing to say? Dennis looked as if I had smacked him on the jaw. But the same jaw set, determined, and he promised me he would try it. As he was going, I said, 'Sympathy is one thing; but you mustn't blame yourself for someone else's personal difficulties. And self-absorbed types are extremely difficult, aren't they?'

'*I'll* try not to be!' he said. And there was the ghost of a grin.

There was another ghost too. Three weeks later, Dennis drew me on one side at the Christmas Fayre and said, 'I did it, Peter. I did what you told me.'

'Did it work? How's the tummy?'

Tummy's all right. And so am I. I went out the night after our chat at the Vicarage. I went past the disused barns and to the far end of Riley's field, right down to the bend in the river. And I shouted out – what you said – 'Sorry, Pa. I should have taken more notice.'

If anyone had seen me or heard me, they'd have thought I was King Lear in bout two of his madness. But it worked – in the strangest way.

I awoke that night and the room was full of light – soft, friendly light, like a summer afternoon. And there was my father. I saw him. It wasn't a dream. I actually saw him. He was young again, as I remember him from when I was a boy. He was always cheerful in those days.

Now here he was again, just like that. We were in the park, and he was laughing and tossing the ball as he used to when we were kids. Then do you know what he did? He came right over to me – sort of out of the park to the bottom of my bed. He smiled – that really happy smile that I'd forgotten he ever had.

And he winked at me. He said clearly, as I'm talking to you now, 'It's OK, Dennis, boy. It's really OK now!' And I felt as if I'd been touched by pure happiness. It was like an absolution.

23   No Black Shawl

'My grandmother knew whenever someone close was about to die. She would always come downstairs that morning in a black shawl.' That was Maureen's story. It was Christmas night and, all the church services being past for another year, we were relaxing with a few parishioners by the fireside. I don't know how it came about that we started on ghost stories; but once we had begun it seemed appropriate enough for the season.

What begins as a laugh can soon turn eerie enough, and it's odd the way a single phrase can conjure an image to make you shudder. 'She had a yellow face and she ran through the town,' and 'Under the pier there was something dead.' Those were two of the opening lines that had put a curl in my hair that particular evening.

But Maureen's psychic gran, was intriguing. I said, 'Your family must have been shaking in their shoes every time the old girl turned up in the black shawl!'

'You know,' said Maureen, 'I'm not sure that she was always right. I think she often was though. But I'm sure I saw her in that shawl on days when nobody popped off. You know what happens: time passes and events get exaggerated.'

This was a rare piece of self-effacement, I thought, in a storyteller – especially in a ghost-storyteller. 'But there's one story about Gran that I can swear to. I know it happened. I can tell you the very day it happened: 15 December 1944.

'I was living in London then, in the East End, with my husband's sister. Her husband had been killed at Anzio, and my Jack was away in Belgium, the Ardennes or somewhere like that. Annie, she was called, my sister-in-law. We got on really well. 'course we were young and both of us working in munitions.'

'And was your grandmother living with you?

No – I was coming to that. She'd been ill and she was convalescing in a home on the other side of town. Finchley, I think. Anyhow, this particular afternoon – 15 December – Annie and I were wondering what we might have for tea. You had to have what you could get in those days. There were such shortages. Hardly any meat – all on rations – coupons, as we used to call them – and the sausage was scandalous: all bread.

We were debating which one of us should run across to Martin's corner shop to see what could be had. Anyway, I said I'd go. I always remember, Annie called after me, 'Fetch us a tin of salmon!' she shouted.

I shouted back: 'You'll be flaming lucky!'

We were in a big house off the Mile End Road. We didn't own it – it was like, flats. And the phone was in the hall. For everybody, you see. Where everybody could get to it.

Just as I was pulling my coat on on my way down the stairs, the phone rang. I picked it up and it was Gran. That was strange anyway because she'd never phoned before. I used to go up and see her on a Saturday or a Sunday and that was that.

But she phoned that day. I said how nice it was to hear her and I hoped there was nothing wrong. 'Wrong?' she said, in a sort of faraway voice. 'Oh, no, dear, there's nothing wrong with me.' *Me*, she said – like that.

We talked about this and that for a minute or two and then I said I'd better be off. 'No, dear, don't go just yet. I don't want you to go just yet.'

I was rather puzzled. We were talking about nothing – just passing the time. I thought I'd better go. I said, 'See you Sunday, Gran.'

'Oh, yes, I do hope so,' she said. And just then there was the mother and father of explosions. The windows were blown in and I felt sure the door had been blasted off its hinges. Martin's shop had been hit by a flying bomb – a V1 or a V2, I don't rightly know which. There was nothing left of the shop. Nothing left of all that corner. Just flattened. If Gran hadn't rung, I'd have been in the shop at the time.

'So the old girl was psychic right enough,' I said.

'Psychic and more besides,' said Maureen. 'Later that afternoon I got another phone call. They'd been trying to get through all day, but there must have been a line down. It was the convalescent home. Gran had died that morning – at ten-past nine. Apparently, she'd got up and said she was going for a little stroll in the garden. The nurse had handed her her black shawl against the cold.

' "No thank you. I shan't be needing that today," said Gran. And those – I have it on authority – were her last words. Three quarters of an hour later she was dead.'

24   A Real Shocker

Parsons deal daily with undertakers. The term itself – 'undertaker' – calls for some explanation. A junior schoolboy in Assembly once told me, with macabre though perfect logic, 'He's the one who takes you under, sir!' It actually means someone who undertakes, on your behalf, to do what is required when there is a death. But there is in modern society a tendency towards euphemisms, and long ago undertakers became Funeral Directors. And a few now have copied their transatlantic brethren and put up signs which say 'Mortician' or even 'Mortician and Embalmer'.

I was lucky. I was privileged to know the most efficient, cheerful and amenable undertaker on – or under – God's earth. This was Dennis Blackstone. Black coat. Black boots. Black tie. Black hearse. But snowy hair. And a red face which paid tribute to country air and the Scotch whisky industry. He had a roguish grin and an impertinent wink. It was said, never without laughter, that he had been 'something of a ladies' man in his day.' If anyone had asked me, I would have said it was still his day when I knew him.

One Christmas I was sitting taking a glass with him by a blazing fire at his cottage – the spacious house that was across the yard from his 'works'.

'You must have had a few eerie experiences in your time, Dennis?'

'Oh, aye. I was called to old Nellie Crawshaw, died aged ninety-one. Or so it was said. She was propped up in her rocking chair and she looked dead enough to me. I turned round to go to the car for my tackle and she called out: "Is that the milkman? You'd better leave an extra pint!" I nearly dropped dead myself, I can tell you.'

He clasped his hands around his glass and warmed to his tale. 'We got stories from the funeral parlour – some too rude to repeat. And from the crematorium, you know, about bodies rising up and opening their eyes as they were being burned. Tosh, most of these tales. But there's one story that unnerved me. It's twelve years since and I still can't shake it off.'

You know there are about six of us undertakers who work this part of Yorkshire. There's me and Jack Steadman, Horace Turner and the Co-op outfit. There used to be more. But you know what they say – it's a dying trade!

Anyhow, I'd been off sick. It was that nasty flu epidemic, about what? – 1969 or thereabouts. I was nearly better, but not quite. Not up to the nitty gritty, laying out and that; but it was a nice morning so I thought I'd make my first appearance at the crem.

It was – I'll never forget it – Emily Singer's funeral and there was a big turn out expected. It was daffodil time, just a couple of weeks this side of Easter. I drove up to the crem in my own car, in good time. I thought I'd pop in nice and early, you know, call and see the Superintendent and let her know I was back in harness – or very nearly.

It had been raining in the night and the sun was dazzling on the path. I nearly bumped into Stan Collyhurst as I was going in. You know big Stan? He's my counterpart in Northallerton. His family have had the undertaker's business there for nearly two hundred years. 'Now then, Dennis,' he said. And he reckoned to punch me in the ribs. It was his style, that. A robust sort, old Stan. He liked his ale, you know; and he was known to take a drop too much now and again. In fact there was a joke that, if you wanted to see the biggest stiff in Northallerton, don't look in Stan's funeral parlour, but look in the Rose and Crown instead and you'd see Stan!

Anyway he was right friendly. 'Are you better, Dennis! I can see you've had a bad do. Don't want you providing business for me yet for a long time!'

And he laughed. Laughed, too much – if you know what I mean. Then he went off down the path towards the office. I went straight round the back to the Verger's little cubby-hole. It was Donald Grey in those days – I don't suppose you ever met him?

Miserable bugger, Don was. He looked like something out

of Dickens. 'It's a bad job, isn't it, Dennis?' were his first words to me.

'What is?' I said.

'Haven't you heard?' he said, dipping his pen in the inkwell; never looking up. 'Stan Collyhurst dropped dead last night. They're bringing him in here, day after tomorrow. Feet first. It's a real shocker.'

25 'I Loved Him ...'

Doris Pickering had turned into a recluse. She lived on the very edge of the parish of Cross Gates in east Leeds – in a cottage in a corner of the first of the fields which marked the open country towards Tadcaster and Boston Spa. She never went out and she survived courtesy of a fleet of home delivery men.

I used to call on her every three months or so. She was not exactly hostile, but most of her conversation was a series of silent nods or shakes of the head. She was surrounded by books and there was no doubting her mental alertness, but her words were so few and far between that it came as a shock to me when she answered my question as to whether she would like me to bring her the Holy Communion: 'Yes,' she said, 'I would like that very much.'

I first took the Sacrament to her one October day in the late 1980s when the rain was driving horizontally in a north-westerly gale. You could see nothing of the fields beyond Doris' cottage: for all anyone might know otherwise, it was like the house at the world's end. I said as much to her as I stepped into the kitchen and hung my waterproofs behind the door. By her usual standards, her reply was effusive: 'It is, Peter, you're right. But, you know, it will soon be the end of the world for me.'

It would be best, I thought, to pursue the subject after we had held the little House Communion service. She led me into the front room where she had placed a linen cloth over the coffee table and lit two small candles. It was, as House Communions often are, intimate and warmhearted. Just Doris and me in the booklined room, with the candlelight flickering into the corners. It made you *feel* the validity of

Christ's saying, 'where two or three are gathered together in my name, there am I in the midst of them.'

She received the Sacrament and then, when I had cleared the table, she resumed what she had been saying earlier: 'It's nearly my time. I am not sorry about it, and I'm not afraid. But before I go, I want to tell you about Bill.'

The room was aromatic from the Communion wine and the doused candles. So, was I really to hear the truth behind all the rumours at last? Everyone knew that Doris, as a young woman, had been married or engaged to be married, but that something had happened to Bill – though I think I was the first to learn that his name was Bill. There was an agreeable haziness about the details which had given to the episode an air of mystique: had he died or, as some said, committed suicide on the eve of his wedding? Was that what had turned Doris into a recluse? Others said he had been sent to prison for some unspeakable – though spoken of often enough – crime. It was all hearsay and conjecture.

Doris left the room and came back with a silver tray on which were coffee cups and a barrel of home-made biscuits.

Bill and I were married. It was 1939, the year war broke out and I was a slip of a thing – only eighteen and we had to get my father's permission. We'd only been wed three months when Bill went off with the British Expeditionary Force to France.

He was rescued at Dunkirk and then was off again to North Africa. Of course, we didn't know he was bound for North Africa at the time. I think in all our married life we had about ten weeks together.

One night – I was living with my mother and father in the middle of Leeds then – I saw Bill in a dream. He was very anxious, waving his arms about, frowning and even crying. I couldn't hear any sound from him but I knew he was trying desperately to get through to me. He was on the troopship, as I saw him in my dream. Then the words came: 'A bomb, Doris! A bomb. For God's sake, take care!'

And there *was* a bomb, the following night. It destroyed the house next door and threw rubble all over us, but no one was seriously hurt. The folks next door were away in the country. The bombers would have been aiming for the railway that ran at the bottom of our street. It was reckoned to be a dangerous spot where we lived, on that account. That's why a lot of people had gone off to stay with relatives or friends in the country. But father always said, 'I went through the 14-18 war, and I'm not going to let Hitler drive me out of my house!'

The next night, I saw Bill again. He was on the ship, as before. He was looking at me. He smiled, but he seemed sad. He had that look on his face – Oh, I don't know: like the hero at the end of a romantic film ...

She had to stop. She was weeping, silently, openly. But there was more than sadness in her tears. She said, 'Oh, I loved him! I loved him so! I could never tell anybody how I loved him – that's why after he'd gone I kept quiet. And I've kept quiet all these years.'

But I wanted to tell someone now my own time's near. That's why I asked you to come.

That second time I saw Bill he waved goodbye. And I knew he was saying he loved me. I felt it. I felt absolutely bathed in his love. It was the most wonderful feeling. There he was on his ship and the sea was a marvellous, calm blue. He was saying goodbye to me. I heard the voice quietly in my head – just like the words about the bomb.

It wasn't long before we learned his ship had been sunk. I didn't need to be told by the telegram. I knew. I knew as sure as you're sitting here now.

I brought her the Holy Communion three times more, and the third time was the Last Rites. She died peacefully in her own home. Her last words to me were: 'Thank you for letting me tell you how much I loved him.'

26   The Lady on the Lawn

Ainscough Manor – what locals used to refer to as 'the big house' – was in my parish near Bolton in Lancashire. It was up on the watery hills, the green tops, between Bolton and Bury and it had belonged to gentlemen farmers for centuries. Rupert Wardle was the occupant at the time of this story. He was a genial, energetic countryman who liked to ride and shoot but who also enjoyed his work with supporters of the Hallé Orchestra in Manchester. In an earlier generation he would have been referred to as 'Squire'.

Rupert was Lay Rector of the parish church, and this old title meant that he was responsible for the upkeep of the fabric of the chancel. In 1974 the Church Council decided to go ahead with substantial repairs to the interior of the south wall and, although no one in modern times would think of holding the Lay Rector liable for the whole cost, it was generally hoped that he would make a contribution. Actually, he volunteered a proportion of the bill before he was even asked. Moreover, he was interested in the details of the repairs, and he told me he had his own ideas about specific improvements. Perhaps I would call and take a drink with him and talk the matter over?

It was July, and Rupert was sitting out on the terrace. He would have been able to watch my approach up the long drive and through the wood planted by his grandfather. I got out of the car and walked to where he was already busy with the iced drinks. It was a hot, buzzing, perfumed day with a feel of eternity about it. 'I took the liberty,' he said, handing me a large Martini.

We sat under the lattice work and picked at olives as we sipped our drinks. Business was always a pleasure with

Rupert, and we had soon concluded the arrangements for the chancel wall. The glasses were refilled. Rupert said, 'You'd never think this old place was haunted, would you? Not on a day like today.'

'Have you met the ghost?'

'Not exactly. Well, I'm not on speaking terms, if that's what you mean.'

He was such an open-hearted man that I'm sure his first words to any ghost would be, 'Hello there! What's yours?' – especially if the ghost were to appear on his own property where hospitality would be a point of honour. He went on: 'I've heard a few bumps and thumps in the night, but then these old houses are so noisy anyway. But I have lost things, and they've turned up somewhere else. My pipe went missing. Then it turned up in a rusting old aquarium which we never use – never have used.

'Miriam has seen something, though – or someone. A shadowy figure a woman, she thinks – on the lawn in the middle of the night. Miriam said the woman was looking up at the high windows, wistfully. Makes me think of 1940s black-and-white films with Margaret Lockwood.'

'What does?' It was Rupert's wife Miriam who had been round the other side of the house in the orchard.

'I was telling Peter about your lady on the lawn.'

Miriam herself looked rather like Margaret Lockwood: darkly romantic and ageless, though she was chiefly known for her potted plants and ginger marmalade – 'the recipe,' she had told me more than once, 'we picked up while we were off the beaten track in Portugal.'

She said, 'Oh, yes, I saw her alright. She looked lost, poor thing. I'm sure it's *her* – the woman the house really belonged to 300 years ago, but she was dispossessed by some legal chicanery. I don't know any more than that – and that's only a guess. If you want to know about Ainscough and its haunted past, ask Rupert to tell you about his grandfather's tale.

'I'm going down to the village, Rupert. Is there anything I can get you?'

Her disappearing car threw up little dust clouds as it went away down the drive. 'Grandfather,' said Rupert, 'used to make our blood run cold when we were children with his stories of the old house. But the most intriguing tale goes back beyond even his day. I suppose I'm talking about the middle of the nineteenth century.'

Anyhow, as Grandpa told it, the Vicar of Ainscough – it was a separate parish in those days, as you know – was out riding one day when he met a lady who said she was the new owner of the manor. The place had lain unoccupied for a few years: there was always some family dispute going on about ownership.

But it was general knowledge that the owner was going to take up residence. Now this woman, if you ask me and by all accounts, was the one whose ghost Miriam says she's seen on the lawn at night. Well, she invited the Vicar to the house for dinner. It was Canon Arnold – Wilfred Arnold – who was Vicar in those days.

As Grandpa said, Canon Arnold went up to the house on the evening appointed, and he was entertained right royally by this lady who poured her heart out over the meal and told him how her good-for-nothing relatives were scheming to deny her out of her rightful inheritance. She was very persuasive, apparently, and, by the end of the dinner *à deux*, she had enlisted the old Canon in her cause. He came away promising he would do all he could to help.

Canon Arnold may have been indiscreet, or he may simply have been seeking advice about how to help the new occupant – I don't know. But he told the lady's tale to a lawyer who lived in the village. The lawyer answered that he would do all he could to help and advise, but surely the Canon had made a mistake: he wasn't talking about Ainscough Hall, but some other place. He must have got the name mixed up with that of somewhere else. 'Because,' said the lawyer, 'Ainscough Hall is still empty. Nobody has taken up residence there yet.'

Grandpa said the old Canon turned white and nearly died of shock. But the two men – Arnold and the lawyer – went up to the house to settle the issue. Looking in through the windows, they saw only dust-sheets and cobwebs. 'But I tell you – that's the dining-room where we took dinner! The chandelier was particularly –'

There was no chandelier. The dining-room was not even furnished with a table. And the lady Arnold had dined with never made an appearance, never took up residence. The tale Grandpa told says she was already dead at the time of the Canon's visit. Her dispute over the ownership of Ainscough

Hall had taken place a hundred years earlier.

I looked across the rose beds to the lawn. The scene was a perfect, broad daylight snapshot of an English summer day. I wondered how it might look in the moonlight.

27   The Hill
by Monte Cassino

'We broke out of the Anzio bridgehead sometime in May 1944 ...' Donald Whiting was giving me the benefit of his war memories again. I didn't mind. He so fleshed out a story, did Donald, that, when he had finished, you came away with the impression that you had been through it all with him.

He was an old man now, and he lived in a magnificent Georgian house – an old people's home – in Harrogate, overlooking the green expanses known locally as 'the Strays'. Donald went all through the war as an infantryman. He was evacuated at Dunkirk, he saw action in North Africa and then he was part of the long push up Italy to the liberation of Rome.

His stories were not so much the blood and guts of warfare as the uncanny communication of men's feelings, or of the spirit of a place; or even an evocation of the weather and the climate. I remember he once said, 'Rome was quiet and hot. No one moved.' You saw the great city instantly, memorably. There were no purple passages in Donald's chat. Usually, also, his tales were down to earth: nothing glamourized, nothing fanciful. But on the Christmas Eve when he told me about the breakout from Anzio, there was an extra, eerie tone in his voice.

'We headed for Monte Cassino, you know, and the battle for the Monastery which was on the commanding heights. On the way, we had to climb another hill. One of those dry, red Italian hills. We got above the line of the olives and suddenly I knew something ... more *saw* something than knew it.

'In my mind's eye I saw lines of German defences. Heavy guns just waiting for us. Soldiers in slit trenches and bunkers, armed to the teeth.'
'What did you do?'

What could I do? I was a corporal infantryman. I'd seen a lot of war. It was hot. The mind plays tricks. What could I do – whistle for the Major and tell him I'd had a premonition and we'd all better turn round and go home? I didn't say anything to anyone. It was a long walk. I rubbed my eyes. I took a swig from my water-bottle. There were flies in the heat.

They knew we were coming. They were waiting, relishing the moment. I even saw one of the front-ranking tanks adjust its main gun.

The picture – I must call it a picture – intensified. I could even see the expressions on the enemy soldiers' faces. I thought I heard snatches of their conversation – about the heat, about booze and Italian girls. What else would a soldier talk about?

I turned round a few times and looked back the way we had come. The valley was rich and there were trails of smoke drifting upwards from small fires. Not fires made by military action. Little, tidy-up blazes lit by the farmers.

I was convinced I was going to die that day.

Then we reached the top of the hill. Not a shot. Not a sound. I was breathless. We were all breathless. And hot – God we were hot. The layout of the enemy troops was exactly as I had 'seen' it. Those steel grey uniforms and hard hats. Tanks in the trees. Shoals of men. They severely outnumbered us. But they never fired a shot.

They were all dead.

28 Only Historical

John Ashby taught history at Whitecrest High School in Bolton when I was Chaplain there. His marriage, of about five years, ran into difficulties and his wife, who worked as an interviewer in the County Court, left him for her boss. John was the fresh-faced English lad; the cricketer and hill walker sort who, when he was not engaged with something more energetic, always had his head in the sports pages. When his wife left, he took it badly.

The disturbing events which happened to John at school may be seen as simply a result of his distress. He was stoical enough. He didn't let his feelings show, but those who knew him understood something of what he was going through. He taught his subject mainly in the middle and upper school and his favourite class, as he told me often, was the fourth year – the ones he was preparing for their GCSE examinations.

'They're interested. And they work,' he said one April morning as we were walking across the field to the dining hall. So they ought. John was an inspirational teacher who could hold a class spellbound with only talk and chalk but who actually offered much more than those things. When they were studying the Civil War, he took his group to all the battle sites in the north of England. And he was the first teacher in Lancashire to organize field trips to the great battlefields of the First World War in France and Belgium.

About three months after Helen had walked out on him, John was teaching that fourth year group when he had what he himself described as a funny turn. One of the girls from the class burst into my room and blurted out that Mr Ashby was ill. I ran next door and found him – not unconscious or in any apparent pain, but standing there, clinging to his desk like

one who, as the psychiatrists say, was 'disorientated for time
and place'. I dismissed the class and got him to sit down. Two
of the girls insisted on staying. 'I'll fetch a drink of water, sir.
He was shouting at us – not at all like Mr Ashby, sir.'

John was dazed as if he had been hit over the head. I asked
him where it hurt. 'It doesn't hurt. But she's gone. Just got up
and left.'

I dismissed the two girls, then I said, 'It's got through to
you, hasn't it? It's bound to. Look, I'll just get someone to
look in on my class and I'll drive you home.' He said nothing
more. Philip Statham, art master, was walking past the
window and I beckoned him. ''Course I'll keep an eye on
your little blighters. First year, aren't they?'

John lived on Turton Moor, overlooking Entwistle
reservoir. We sat in his kitchen drinking coffee and looking
out at the black and bright Spring day. It was a lovely view –
like an English watercolour. And so quiet.

He seemed to come round. 'It's not what you think,' he
said.

I wasn't talking about Helen when I said she'd got up and left.
Not *my* Helen, that is. I was teaching my lot about the Civil
War, and I seemed to see them all in their rows in front of me,
in period costume. I thought I was going mad.

They were all talking a kind of Bunyanese, just like
something out of *Pilgrim's Progress*. It was unnerving, I can
tell you. Well, I thought I was going to faint. I had to try to
control them, somehow. They were getting unruly – all
talking at once. I'm afraid I shouted at them. I felt I was losing
control, not just of them but of myself. I seemed to be having
a blazing row with one of them in particular: Helen – Helen
Fisher. I must have really got through to her because she burst
into tears and stormed out. I was left calling out. 'Come back!
Come back!' I know I was. I could hear myself. But it did no
good. You know what it's like when you yell in a
nightmare?

The rest of the class – still in their seventeenth-century togs –
you must think I'm barmy! – seemed to be trying to calm me
down, to say that it didn't matter if Helen Fisher left. Let her
go.

And then a voice said out loud, clear as anything, 'Now
look who's here! It's Carol.' And a young woman came

through the door and sat where Helen Fisher had been sitting. I suppose that must have been when you came in, Peter.

She was very pretty. Anyway, it seemed to calm everybody down when she came in. I feel such a fool – a fraud, really. Thanks for bringing me home. Apologize to the Head for me, will you – and to the fourth year – and say I'll be in in the morning.

What strange effects stress can produce! John did come in the next day and he seemed perfectly well again. The real Helen Fisher – the bright girl in 4X – had not walked out of John's lesson at all: that much must have been part of his temporary delirium. And no new girl, Carol came to join the class.

His wife, Helen, did not return. But, before Christmas of that same year, he was remarried – to a young woman called Carol.

29   Adam's First Wife

Ghostly recollections are like sexual reminiscences: the most hauntingly exciting are not always the ones that are most explicit. Hint and innuendo, atmosphere and suggestion are powerful stimulants to the imagination and the emotions. I know a lady who was – still is – haunted.

There is no ghost like a great white sheet flapping about her bedroom. No dead bodies walk along her landing at night. She is haunted nevertheless. As she explained to me: 'It's like an addiction. Something alien has entered my life, and I know I shall never be free of it.'

Jane Crosby, spinster of the parish and sewing-machine saleslady at a Leeds department store, can put a date and a place to her sense of having been invaded by strangeness. I went to ask her for a donation to the Tower Restoration Fund one summer day and found her sitting out in the garden under a willow tree.

'It was a day like this,' she said. 'Not too hot. Sunny, with a gentle breeze. Perfect English summertime, in fact. Quite the farthest thing from thoughts of ghosts and ghoulies.'

I was still at home, living with my parents in Cheltenham at the time. They were getting on in years, and they didn't feel up to taking a whole week's holiday abroad as they used to. Dad was happy enough pottering about in the garden, and Mum and I decided we'd take a few days' outings: go on a coach trip one day, stay at home the next – that sort of thing.

There was an outing one day to the Malvern Hills – Elgar territory. It was a bus ride and a guided tour of Great Malvern, the ancient parish church and all that.

It was glorious. A slight haze over the seven hills. I've always thought that landscape goes perfectly with Elgar's

music. Nostalgia. Anyhow, we arrived and had our lunch in
the Tudor Cafe, then strolled out over the lower slopes away
from the traffic. It had got quite hot by this time and I
remember there were lots of butterflies and bumble bees.
Everything was so drowsy. We didn't try to hurry.

There are some beautiful old houses on those slopes. Really
elegant. Mum and I were fantasizing about being able to
afford one! We took our time. Our footsteps crackled over the
gravel path. The air was full of the scent of wild flowers.
Everyone was amiable, relaxed – half-asleep, if the truth be
told. You know how voices sound quiet and distant in that
sort of warmth?

Suddenly, I was brought up with a start. It was like a cold
blast in the face. I was wide awake now all right! Mum said,
'What's the matter? Are you ill?'

I wasn't ill. I was terrified. But why? Nothing had altered.
There we were among the trees and white painted houses as
before. The birds were singing and the sun still shone. But
there was one thing new. Right in front of us was a cottage –
more than a cottage, but not quite a villa.

There were rose trees on either side of it, and poplars stood
behind it. A real chocolate-box picture, if you like. But that
house scared the life out of me. I don't know why. I didn't
know then and I still don't know, ten years later. It was an
atmosphere. So powerful. Overwhelming. Well, it overwhelmed me all right, I don't mind admitting it.

I felt drawn to it. And yet, as we got closer, I was repelled.
Scared. Scared stiff. It wasn't as if it was a special place, a
museum, part of the Elgar heritage or anything like that. It
was a very nice private house, and that was all. There was a
man in the garden mowing the lawn, a pipe in his mouth. But
even the drone of the mower was part of the disturbing
atmosphere.

'What's the matter with you? What's the matter?' my
mother kept on at me. But I only shushed her and gritted my
teeth as we walked by the front gate. 'Lilith', it said on the
gate. 'Lilith' – that was its name. Of course, I've found out
since who Lilith was. According to an old legend, she was
Adam's first wife.

The road took a steep turn at this point and we paused to
catch our breath. I could look down on the place now and see
the whole layout of the house and garden. We rounded a bend
and the place was out of sight at last. Slowly, I recovered my
wits.

'Just the house,' I answered my mother. 'The house. An atmosphere to it. It reminds me of something, but I don't know what. You know what it's like when there's a word on the tip of your tongue and you can't spit it out? Well, it's like that.'

'How strange!' said Mum. 'I've never known you have creepy thoughts like that before.' And she was right. I wasn't given to psychic feelings, second sight or anything of the kind. That's why it came as such a shock, I suppose. It was something strange to me – out of the blue, literally.

Now here's the weird bit. I was disconcerted by the place, but I was fascinated by it too. I wanted to return and take a second look. I needed to know more about the place. It was as if it had some special significance for me. When we got home, Mum told Dad. They didn't laugh at me. Actually, they were intrigued because their plain Jane had had something out of the ordinary happen to her.

We didn't speak of it again, but I wasn't able to forget it. I brooded, until I knew I must go back.

It was winter. I made my own way to the Malverns in the car. How different it all was! The tops of the hills were hidden in mist. The rain lashed into the windscreen. Everyone carried a coloured umbrella, or so it seemed – so different from my summer visit.

I found the gravel path and parked the car. For a minute or two I sat there, daring myself to get out. Then I laughed – made myself laugh out loud, as a bit of bravado. I walked up the hill in the rain. So different from my last visit. It was cold and the rain stung your face in the wind.

I was feeling pretty stupid actually. Why had I made such a fuss? Why, come to think of it, had I taken a day off work in January to drive out into the country in freezing wet weather? Then I turned the corner and there the cottage was. I nearly passed out at the sight of it. It was as if a stone had rolled across the pit of my stomach.

I stood staring at the cottage, the raindrops running down my glasses. 'Lilith', it said. I seemed to hear a voice in my head – not out loud, you understand, nothing daft like that! – but clear as anything all the same: 'Lilith,' it said, 'Adam's first wife'.

I turned away, my heart pounding. I didn't run exactly. But I didn't hang about. I didn't see another soul.

I've been back a few times. How can I explain it – it draws me. I'm completely schizo about the place. When I'm there I go to pieces – there's no way you'd get me inside! Then, when I'm away from it, I miss it. I have to go back. Then I'm scared out of my wits again. And so it goes on.

I've actually talked to the owner – the man with the lawnmower. Nice ordinary retired chap. His wife deadheading the roses – asked me in for a cup of tea. No chance! I made an excuse. Hope I didn't sound impolite. The name? The old chap said it was called that when he moved in – and he'd been there thirty years. Yes, he knew the origin of the name, but, as he said, he'd never really given it a second thought.

The house had been built in the 1870s when it was part of a farm. There have been four owners. And that's the beginning and end of all I know about the place. No sensational happenings there as far as I can discover. No murders, suicides, fires – nothing at all out of the ordinary.

'Will you go back again, d'you think?' I asked.

'I say I won't. But I know I will.'

As I said at the beginning, no spectres or spooks here but something certainly that is not easily understood. What made Jane feel so fascinated and at the same time oppressed by an English country cottage she had never seen before?

There is a postscript to this story which may not have even the slightest significance. But six months after my conversation with Jane that summer day in her garden, she got married – at the age of thirty-eight. He was a pleasant fellow: a solicitor, called Adam. He had been married before. His first wife, Lilian, had committed suicide.

30   Amy's Husband

Some places become theme parks without trying. Tockwith, a village nine miles to the west of York, is close to the site of the Civil War battle of Marston Moor which took place in 1644. Half the streets in the village's new housing development are called 'Prince Rupert' and the other half 'Fairfax', after the names of notable protagonists in the bloodletting.

Each year the historical society the Sealed Knot come and re-enact the old battle on 2 July, and late at night you can still see costumed Roundheads and Cavaliers drinking together outside the local pubs. When I was Vicar there, I used to answer, if I could, the queries of tourists – mostly American – who had bothered to make the short excursion to Tockwith from the more renowned historical sites in York.

Sometimes these visitors would come to church, if they happened to be in the village when there was a service. In July 1977, there was a special service to mark the Silver Jubilee of the Queen, and Tockwith Church was packed for Evensong. Afterwards, when the congregation had drifted away, the notes of Parry's *Jerusalem* still resounding in their ears, an American couple, Amy and Clive, stayed behind and asked me the usual questions about Cromwell and King Charles. Amy and Clive, let it be said, were of the better informed class of visitor. The worse informed would ask such questions as, 'And where does Julius Caesar fit in to your Civil War? Was he on the King's side?'

It was a mellow evening and I walked with these two American visitors as far as the Boot and Shoe. We sat at a table ouside and watched the sky darken gradually through a dozen shades of blue. The country is flat in those parts and so the skyscapes are frequently more spectacular than the landscape. Indeed, in high summer the sky fills seven tenths of your vision and it never gets completely dark.

Amy had been reading up about the Battle of Marston Moor and she was clearly very moved by the whole story of the Civil War. 'You're such a little old country to be having wars among yourselves. And who could dream of going to war in such lovely surroundings?'

'We Yanks fought in the Bay of Naples, honey,' said Clive.

It was not the usual sort of touristy conversation. Clive, a lawyer, was fascinated by the religious dimension of the Civil War as it found expression in the doctrine of the Divine Right of Kings, and also in the strict Puritanism of the Model Army. I remember that we discussed the abstruse theological teaching of Predestination and Election to Grace for more than two hours.

But something deeper than historical curiosity had got through to Amy. She seemed transfixed, hypnotised by the atmosphere of that ancient struggle – almost as if, when she gazed to her right up the Marston Road, she saw it all enacted before her. Not, carnival style, by the Sealed Knot's rumbustious members, but really in its whole tragic weight.

Amy's intensity spread over all three of us. There was a sense of the uncanny, the atmospheric seriousness of that troubled 2 July in 1644. It was odd. Without anyone's actually mentioning it, there developed a reflective reverent 'feel' to the evening. 'Feel' is right: we all felt it.

It was almost midnight by the time they left. They were planning to stay in England for a few more days: the usual tour – London, Bath, Stratford, Chester and York. A week later, I received a letter from Amy. It was postmarked Dorchester. Obviously they had been drawn into a Thomas Hardy excursion. The letter had the same atmosphere about it as our conversation ouside the Boot and Shoe.

She said that England – and particularly the York area – had changed her; that it was as if, as she put it, 'Something is travelling along with me. Something that wasn't there before. Or someone!' Clive had told her not to be so dumb: that she had fallen for 'The museum culture'. But Amy said in her letter, 'It's like our airplane was a time machine. When you told us about the Battle of Marston Moor, it was as if it had just happened that day. And I had been in it – not as a spectator but as someone taking part. God alone knows whose side I was on!'

She ended her letter with rather fulsome thanks and another couple of stanzas in praise of little old England. That, I thought, would be the end of my acquaintance with Clive and Amy, but in October of that same year I received this letter from Amy in St Joseph, Missouri:

Someone *did* come back with me. It's the presence I felt at my elbow all that evening as we talked outside your bar. And it caused some trouble, I can tell you. I became incredibly sad, sort of heavy. The doc gave me pills and a checkover, but no good. I wasn't sleeping. There was this someone – from the old battle – beside me the whole time. And I just knew there was something I had to do for him.

A girlfriend sent me to her hypnotherapist, and I was regressed to 1644 in England. I saw a man – one of the King's men – in the field. It was nearly sunset and he was wounded. He looked so sorrowful. The hypnotherapist asked me to ask if there was anything I could do. So I did. And he replied, 'Tell my wife, Amy, that I love her.'

I said, 'How did you know my name?' He said, 'Not you. Not your name. My wife's name is Amy.'

I remembered it all when I woke up. And, of course, I told Clive all about it too. The soldier's presence became stronger as the days went by, and I just knew he had died in that battle. Just think – poor Amy never saw her husband alive again. It got right through to me somehow. I thought my heart would break.

The hypnotherapist asked if we were church people. I said we went along sometimes. So he said I should get the minister to call and ask him to say a prayer for the repose of that wounded soldier. I never discovered his name.

There was one place where his presence and the sense of him was particularly strong and that was in the hall between the kitchen and lounge. The minister – well, I thought he would think I was nuts. But he didn't. He came along last Tuesday and we all said prayers for 'Amy's husband'.

It was as if a great weight had been lifted off my chest. There's just peace now, and calm. And lovely recollections of summer evenings in England.

31   He Cries All the Time

There was an old terrace house by the side of the Scarborough railway line in Crossgates, Leeds, which over the years had been the scene of ghostly events. In the 1960s it featured in one of the popular Sunday newspapers as a place infested with poltergeist activity. Various mediums and exorcists had been called in to try to quieten the house, and, indeed, there was a lull in the spooky goings on – for a while, at least.

The immediate cause of the disturbance was reckoned to have been a boy of about fourteen who was living there. Adrian was an albino and because of his startling appearance he was sometimes teased at school. One of my predecessors, a Curate in the parish, had suggested that the poltergeist activity was a result of Adrian's emotional distress. This sounded quite plausible and it was backed up by a psychologist's report.

In 1969, Adrian and his family left the area and went to live in Worksop. A few years later, Crossgates learned of a tragedy: Adrian and his mother were killed in a car accident on the M1. Almost at once the disturbances began again in their old house.

The new occupants called in a faith healer they had met at a Pentecostal Christian tabernacle in the middle of Leeds. They also asked me – hedging their bets, as it were – to come and say some prayers. I did as they had asked, but the disturbances continued. So I went to see the people again and told them that I could call in the official diocesan exorcist and that he would certainly quieten the place.

It was not a happy time in that street. The new family at Adrian's old house did not get on with their neighbours.

There was talk of colour prejudice and various sorts of victimization. They decided, after not many months, to leave: 'We know when we're not wanted. We'll clear off. Might as well leave the ghost as a house-warming present to the new owners!' The new owners were a long time coming. The house lay empty for almost eighteen months.

When the new people, the Atkinsons, finally arrived, they settled into the neighbourhood as if they had been born there. Donald was a salesman, and his wife Penny was a vigorous voluntary worker. In a matter of weeks she had made herself known to the women's organizations in the parish and offered her services as assistant to the Captain of the Girl Guides. Donald and Penny had two children: Louise, who was doing her 'A' levels and Jeremy, aged eleven, who was in the top class at the local Junior School.

When they had been in the house for about three months, I paid them a call. 'Before you ask,' said Donald, 'we've heard all the rumours and old wives' tales; but we've never been bothered by anything going bump in the night, have we Penny?'

Louise, who was planning to become a microbiologist, said, 'Ghosts – things like that – only appear to people stupid enough to believe in them. I don't believe in them.'

'Good old Louise!' said Penny. 'At least we know where *you* stand.'

'How about you, Jeremy?' said Donald.

'I think ghosts appear because they need our help. I don't think there's any reason to be scared of them. It's silly really. I mean, I might as well be scared of the Vicar.'

Jeremy was a thoughtful boy and, when he began Secondary School, he joined my Confirmation Class. It was autumn and the classes met on Thursday evenings in the vicarage. After one class had finished, he stayed behind and asked if he could have a word with me about something in private. 'You know when I said ghosts came because they need our help? I think I've met a ghost and he's incredibly sad. He cries all the time.'

'And where does this take place, Jeremy?'

'We burn the old coal fire at our house, you know. Dad says he's going to rip it out and have gas-fired central heating put in. Well, Louise and I like the old fire. So I said to Dad,

"Well, at least let's keep the fire until we've used all the coal."
And he said we could.

'There's more dust than coal in the cellar now. I like to go
down there and use the big sieve and separate the little bits of
the coal from the dust. That's when I saw him – sitting on the
old washtub at the other end of the cellar. I often see him, but
he makes me sad – he's very upset about something.'

'What's he like?'

'That's just it. He's a bit strange. He's got loads of really
white hair and pink eyes.'

I went and spoke to the whole family. After that, I said
prayers in the cellar for the repose of the souls of the
departed. The house has been quiet since that day. They have
gas-fired central heating in now.